A Story Through TIME

Text, maps, ompilation and design by

Patrick J Mc Keever, Ph.D

Illustrations and design by

Janis Smyth, MDes (RCA)

©Landscapes From Stone 1999

Introduction

Ireland is justifiably proud of its rich heritage of scenic landscapes. From the broad expanse of the Central Plain to the heights of Macgillicuddy's Reeks in Co. Kerry the diversity of landscapes has inspired both locals and visitors alike. Perhaps nowhere is this great variety of scenery more apparent than in the northern part of the island. Here the splendour of the Glens of Antrim, the Causeway Coast (1), the Donegal Highlands, Yeat's Country, and the Sperrin and the Mourne Mountains are well known. Combined with the gentle drumlin country of Cavan, Monaghan and Armagh, the lakelands of Fermanagh and the lowlands around Lough Neagh the region presents an ever changing vista to the traveller. But how many travellers of the region realise that this variety of scenery primarily reflects the region's great diversity of geology which forms the very foundation of the country? The geological map of the region resembles a patchwork of colours where each colour represents a different rock type . These rocks span a time period that is immense and beyond human comprehension. By unravelling this geological history we can begin to understand the formation of the landscapes of Ireland (north). This story has been billions of years in the making and tells of ancient lost oceans, immense deserts, drifting continents, towering mountain ranges, erupting volcanoes and thick sheets of ice. This may sound too fantastic to be believable but each of these events left behind evidence of its passing and this proof is all around us in the rocks and landscape. This book aims to recount the extraordinary geological history of Ireland (north) and the formation of our "Landscapes From

1 - The Giants Causeway. Co. Antrim

Stone". It is intended as an accompaniment to the "Landscapes from Stone" map published by the Geological Surveys and which highlights many sites where the evidence of our geological history can be seen and examined. As on the map, the region of Ireland (north) has been divided into 14 areas on the basis of a particular geological event, or series of events, which imparted a special character to that area. In this book these areas are arranged in order of the age of that key geological event. However, as is evident from both the geological map and the "Landscapes from Stone" map each area contains rocks of different ages and a comprehensive geological history of each would fill many books this size! Nevertheless, by concentrating on one event in each area we can build up the story of the formation of the region and the formation of our "Landscapes From Stone".

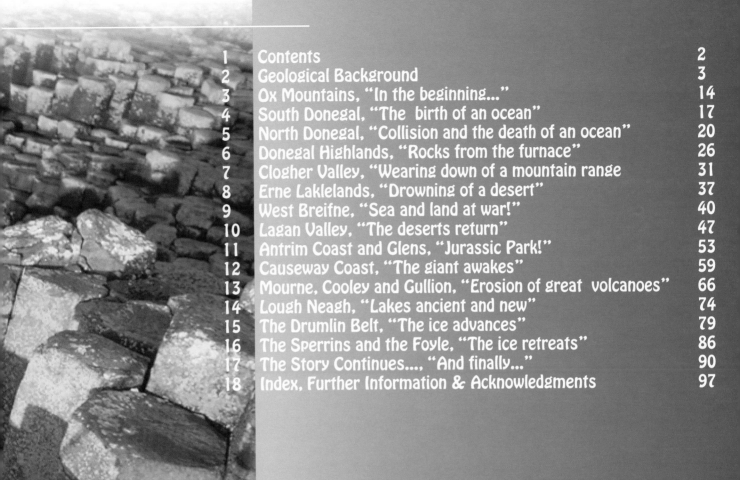

Contents

Landscapes from Stone

Geological Background and key principles

Before we can begin to unravel the story of our Landscapes From Stone there are perhaps a few questions that need to be answered. Millions of years ago? How can you tell? Ice sheets, erupting volcanoes, vast deserts? How do we know that? Drifting continents? How is that possible?

Millions of years ago? How can you tell?

The life span of the average human being is currently between 70 and 80 years. Archaeologists tell us that Man first arrived in Ireland some 9000 years ago. By contrast, geologists tell us that the basalt columns of the Giant's Causeway are 60,000,000 years old, the oldest rocks in Ireland are over 1,700,000,000 years old and the Earth is some 4,600,000,000 years old! Given that the average human is lucky to live to be 80 years old, how is it possible for us to comprehend the much greater ages of the rocks? Perhaps one way of doing so is to compare the age of the Earth to a 24 hour day. Using this comparison, the Earth formed at midnight (00.00hrs) as a molten sphere orbiting around the newly born Sun (2). The first living cells didn't appear until 7.00am, primitive green algae didn't evolve until 10.40am, life on land didn't appear until 10pm and Man first evolved only a minute or so to midnight (24.00hrs)! But how do we know this?

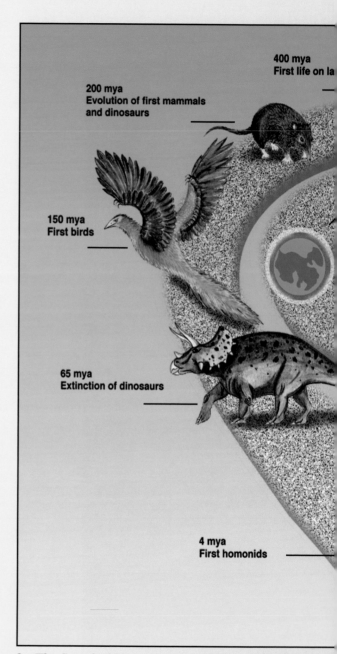

400 mya
First life on la

200 mya
Evolution of first mammals and dinosaurs

150 mya
First birds

65 mya
Extinction of dinosaurs

4 mya
First homonids

2 - The Spiral of Time: key events in Earth history

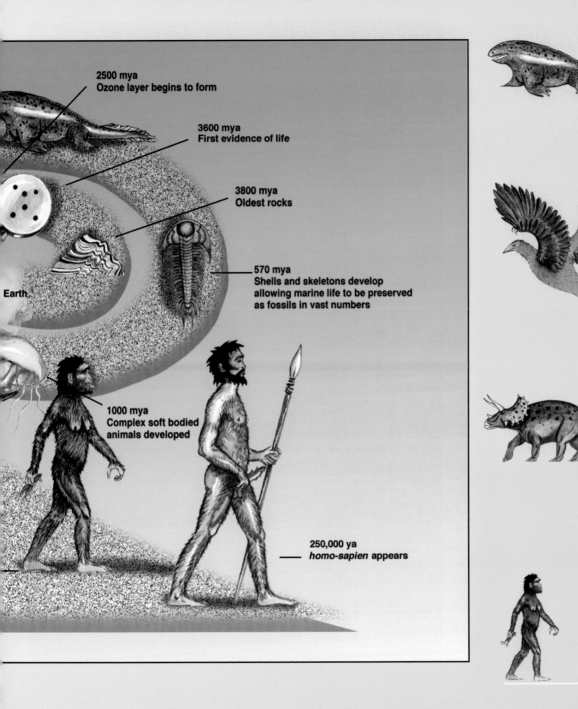

2500 mya
Ozone layer begins to form

3600 mya
First evidence of life

3800 mya
Oldest rocks

570 mya
Shells and skeletons develop
allowing marine life to be preserved
as fossils in vast numbers

Earth

1000 mya
Complex soft bodied
animals developed

250,000 ya
homo-sapien appears

Many rocks contain naturally radioactive components (or minerals), that is over time some of their constituent minerals gradually change composition from one form to another. By knowing the rate of change and by measuring how much of the original component is left we can calculate the age of the rock. Following a great explosion in the diversity of life some 545 million years ago many rocks also contain fossils. Fossils are the remains or traces of plants and animals that lived at the time these rocks were being formed. By knowing the age of the rock in which these fossils occur, we can also build up a picture of how life has evolved on Earth over the great expanse of time.

Because geologists tend to think of time not in minutes or hours or weeks but in many millions of years, they have devised a system where time is split up into individual periods (3). These periods are based on the timing of particular geological events, or the dominance of particular plants and animals or, more usually, by a combination of both. Consequently geologists refer to the Cambrian Period for rocks from 545 to 495 million years ago or to the Jurassic, for rocks from 205 to 142 million years ago. Periods are also grouped into the much longer Eras. For instance, the Mesozoic era includes the Triassic, Jurassic and Cretaceous Periods and lasted from 248 to 65 million years ago. The end of the Cretaceous Period, and therefore the end of the Mesozoic Era, is marked by the

Age million years	Era	Period	Events Relating To Ireland (North)
— 1.6	Cenozoic (Recent Life)	Quaternary (Fourth Period)	Ice sheets periodically advance and retreat over the region, moulding the landscape.
— 23		Neogene (New stock)	Deposition of clays and lignite around Lough Neagh and Ballymoney, Co Antrim.
— 65		Palaeogene (Ancient stock)	Formation of North Atlantic Ocean leads to widespread volcanism in north-east Ireland.
— 142	Mesozoic (Middle Life)	Cretaceous (Creta - Latin for chalk)	Irish landmass submerged beneath a warm, shallow sea allowing formation of vast deposits of chalk. Period ends with mass extinction of life.
— 206		Jurassic (Jura- area of Switzerland)	Pangea begins to fragment. Mudstones deposited on floor of shallow sea. Dinosaurs become dominant form of life on land.
— 248		Triassic (Trias - from the Latin for three)	Desert landscape flooded by shallow seas. Formation of salt deposits in east Antrim. First true mammals appear.
— 290	Palaeozoic (Ancient Life)	Permian (Perm - town in Russia)	Arid conditions return. Formation of the supercontinent Pangea is complete. Mass extinction of life.
— 354		Carboniferous (after carbon-rich coal beds)	The desert is flooded by a shallow sea. Erosion of Caledonian Mountains leads to delta formation, swamps and the development of coal. First reptiles appear.
— 417		Devonian (Devon - area of England)	Final formation of the Caledonian Mountains is followed by a hot arid climate. First amphibians colonise the land.
— 443		Silurian (Silures - ancient Welsh tribe)	Continental collision generates magma leading to the intrusion of granites.
— 495		Ordovician (Ordovices - ancient Welsh tribe)	The Iapetus Ocean contracts and continental collision leads to the metaporhosis of the Dalradian sediments.
— 545		Cambrian (Cambria - Latin for Wales)	Opening of the Iapetus Ocean.
— 1000	Proterozoic (First Life)	Precambrian (Before the Cambrian)	Deposition of the Dalradian sediments of Donegal, Derry and Tyrone from 700 to 600 million years ago.
— 2000			Continental collision leads to formation of gabbro and serpententite in the Ox Mountains over 1,000 million years ago.
			Formation of the oldest rocks in Ireland (Inishtrahull off Co. Donegal and north Mayo) some 1,750 million years ago.
— 3000			Life has created enough free oxygen to allow the development of a protective ozone layer in Earth's atmosphere around 2,700 million years ago.
			First evidence of primitive life is 3,600 million years old.
— 4000			Oldest known rocks on Earth around 4,000 million years old.
— 4600			Formation of the Solar System around 4,600 million years ago.

3 - The Geological Column

5

extinction of many groups of plants and animals, most notably the Dinosaurs. The end of the older Permian Period, 248 million years ago, is marked by a much larger mass-extinction of life when over 90% of all species are believed to have become extinct. This event also marks the end of the Palaeozoic Era.

Ice sheets, erupting volcanoes, vast deserts? How do we know that?

Today on our planet many natural processes operate which gradually, or in some cases catastrophically, change the appearance of the landscape. High mountains are worn down by wind, rain and ice, and rivers carry away the debris before depositing it elsewhere. Scorching winds mould the sands of deserts while ocean storms crashing against coastlines can dramatically, and quickly, change the landscape. Earthquakes, volcanoes and flash-floods too can alter the appearance of the landscape in a matter of minutes. These processes, which we see operating today, leave behind unique landforms or rock types. These same processes have also operated in the past and then, just as now, they created new landforms and rock types. By identifying these ancient landforms and rocks we can tell what process created them and even what climatic conditions were like at that time.

Drifting continents? How is that possible?

We often tend to joke about the Irish weather, "...if you don't like it, just wait a minute or so and it'll change!" One predictable thing about our weather is its variability. Our present climate is mild and wet but changeable and the beautiful landscape it has helped mould has been admired by many generations. But geologists tell us that the landscapes of Ireland (north) span a timescale of some 1,500 million years and evidence from the rocks of the region show that during that time Ireland has witnessed many changes of climate and many dramatic geological events. There is evidence of continental collision (Donegal), ancient oceans (Cavan - Down) and tropical seas (Sligo), hot deserts (Belfast), ice ages (Sperrins) and volcanic eruptions (Antrim) to name but a few. But why has Ireland witnessed so many different climates and environments? The answer lies in the Earth itself.

The Earth is not a solid sphere of rock but is made up of different layers. At the centre is a solid core of iron and nickel around which is a thick hot, mantle. Overlying this is the very thin surface layer of solid rock we call the crust. Although the mantle is mostly solid, because of the intense heat and pressure found in the mantle it can behave like a liquid. As such convection currents operate allowing the transfer of hot material from one part of the mantle to another. Because the overlying crust (upon which we all live) is so thin in relation to the mantle these currents have broken the crust up into a number of large segments or "plates". These plates move relative to each other and it is along the boundaries between plates that we get zones of earthquakes and volcanoes. Where plates move apart, molten material from the mantle wells up to fill the gap thus creating new crust. This process is happening today on the ocean floor along the middle of the Atlantic (4). Here the North American and South American plates are moving away from the Eurasian and African plates as the Atlantic Ocean widens by a few centimetres every year. Elsewhere plates collide and crust is destroyed as one plate is forced, or subducted, beneath the other. The Indian plate has crashed into the Eurasian plate creating the Himalayas in the process. The Nazca plate (which underlies part of the Pacific Ocean) is colliding with the South American plate and being subducted beneath it (5). This collision has led to the formation of the Andes Mountains. Sometimes plates simply move past each other without any

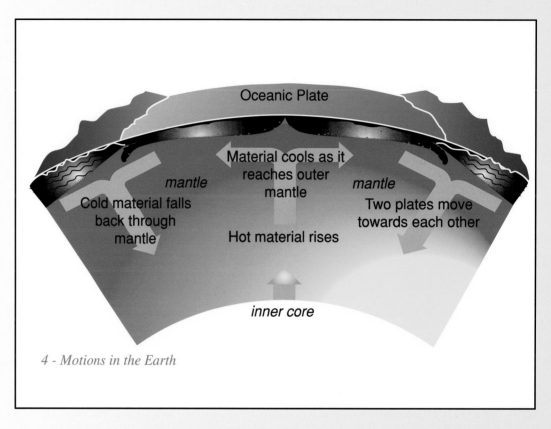

Oceanic Plate

Material cools as it reaches outer mantle

mantle

Cold material falls back through mantle

Hot material rises

mantle

Two plates move towards each other

inner core

4 - Motions in the Earth

creation or destruction of crust. In California, the Pacific and North American plates move past each other in this way. Each time they move the ground above shakes explaining why this area is so prone to earthquakes. Although plate movement is slow, over millions of years not only does it cause the oceans and continents to change shape and size relative to each other it also causes the levels of the land and sea to change and can lead to great changes in climate (6). Consequently, Ireland has, at various times, been under water, subjected to volcanic activity and been involved in major continental collisions to name but a few. Furthermore, as some rocks form they become magnetised. This is because they contain small amounts of iron and other magnetic minerals. By measuring the magnetism in these ancient rocks, geologists can also track the position of these rocks, and therefore the continents, over time. Evidence for all these events is found in the landscape around us and in the rocks beneath our feet. It is this fascinating story of the evolution of Ireland into the island we are familiar with today that can be read in our "Landscapes From Stone".

5 - Plate subduction. Along the western coast of South America the oceanic Nazca plate, which underlies part of the eastern Pacific Ocean, is being subducted beneath continental crust

Pacific Ocean

Nazca Plate

Andes

South American Plate

Subduction at 15cm per year

Melting Zone

Rocks

The geological map of Ireland (north) shows that there are many different rock types across the region (7). However all these rocks, along with rocks everywhere, can be collected together into three main groups: igneous, sedimentary and metamorphic. **Igneous** rocks are formed from the cooling of molten material or magma (8). If the magma cools below the surface of the Earth we get intrusive igneous rocks (e.g. granite, gabbro) whereas if the magma erupts onto the surface as lava extrusive igneous rocks are formed (e.g. basalt, rhyolite). **Sedimentary** rocks are usually formed from the consolidation of material such as mud, silt and sand that is deposited by rivers, wind, and ocean currents (e.g. mudstone and sandstone). Such rocks are usually deposited in layers, or beds, and under normal circumstances where we see layers of rock we can assume that the oldest bed is at the bottom and the youngest is at the top. Sometimes the dead remains of organisms can collect in huge amounts and can get consolidated into rock (e.g. coal, chalk). **Metamorphic** rocks are simply igneous or sedimentary rocks that have been changed, or metamorphosed, into a new rock. This can happen if the rock is heated such as when molten magma rises and comes into contact with cooler rock (e.g. hornfels), or when the rock is subjected to high pressures such as those experienced during continental collision (e.g. gneiss, slate). In these circumstances layers of rock can become greatly distorted (folded), fractured (faulted) or even turned upside down (9).

6 - *The Earth through geological history. Over eons of time as the crustal plates have drifted over the surface of the Earth so the appearance of our planet from space has changed.*

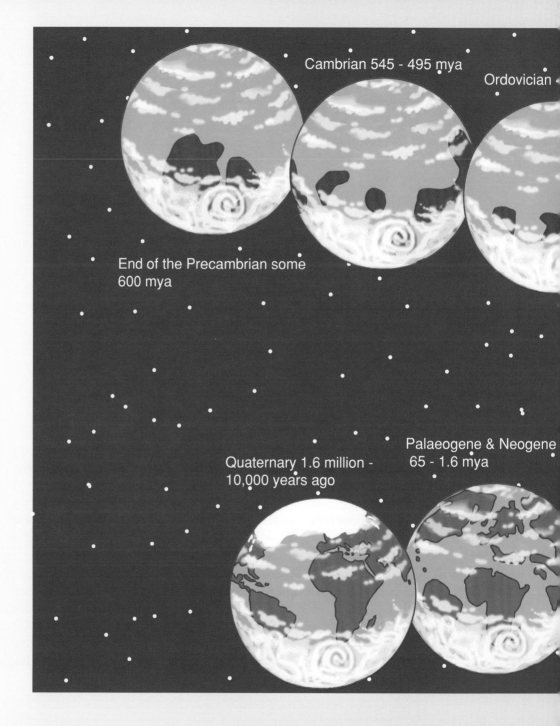

Cambrian 545 - 495 mya

Ordovician

End of the Precambrian some 600 mya

Palaeogene & Neogene 65 - 1.6 mya

Quaternary 1.6 million - 10,000 years ago

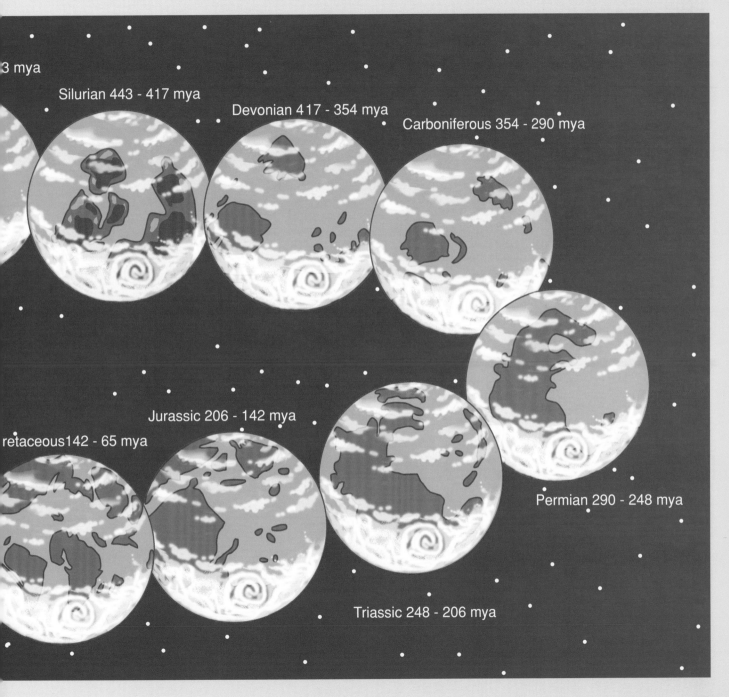

3 mya

Silurian 443 - 417 mya

Devonian 417 - 354 mya

Carboniferous 354 - 290 mya

Permian 290 - 248 mya

Triassic 248 - 206 mya

Jurassic 206 - 142 mya

retaceous142 - 65 mya

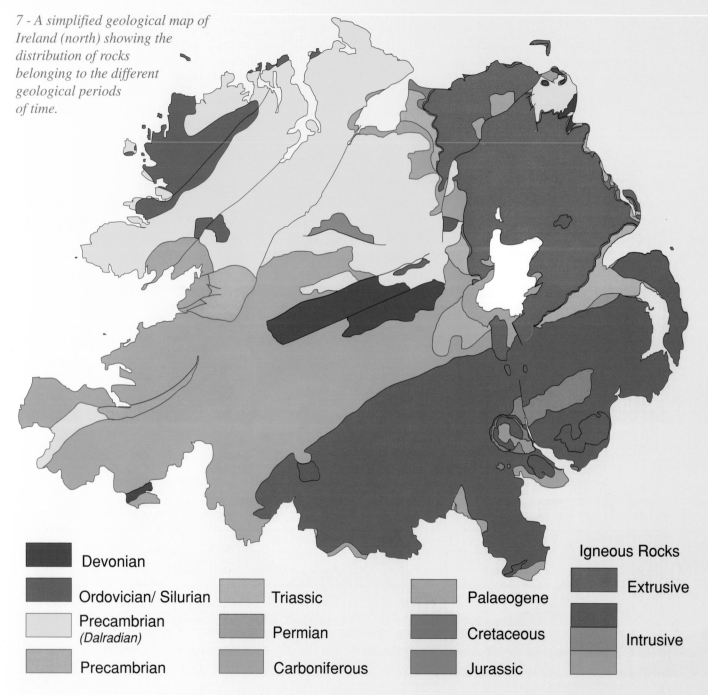

7 - A simplified geological map of Ireland (north) showing the distribution of rocks belonging to the different geological periods of time.

Devonian

Ordovician/ Silurian

Precambrian *(Dalradian)*

Precambrian

Triassic

Permian

Carboniferous

Palaeogene

Cretaceous

Jurassic

Igneous Rocks

Extrusive

Intrusive

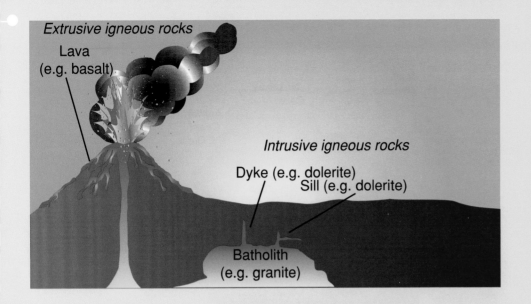

Extrusive igneous rocks

Lava
(e.g. basalt)

Intrusive igneous rocks

Dyke (e.g. dolerite)

Sill (e.g. dolerite)

Batholith
(e.g. granite)

8 - *As molten magma cools it forms igneous rocks. If the magma cools below the surface of the Earth it forms intrusive igneous rocks such as granite. If the magma erupts onto the surface as lava, it cools to form extrusive igneous rocks such as basalt.*

9- *Under the great temperatures and pressures experienced by rocks during plate collision, they can become deformed and metamorphosed into new rock types such as gneiss. Contact with molten magma can also cause rocks to metamorphose.*

Intense heat and pressure alters pre-existing rocks into metamorphic rocks such as schist and gneiss

12

Now that we have some background information to the "hows" and "whys" of geology, we can start to unravel the fantastic story of Ireland (north), its "Landscapes From Stone" and their fascinating journey through time. As mentioned in the introduction the region has been split up into 14 areas defined on the basis of their landscape (10). In almost all cases the distinctive nature of each of these landscape-based areas owes much of its existence to the underlying geology. Each of these areas contains evidence of at least one chapter in the long story of the development of the landscapes of the region, from continental collision in North Donegal to volcanic eruptions along the Causeway Coast. Everywhere however, the development of the landscape has been further moulded by the action of ice sheets and glaciers during the last Ice Age and in two areas it is the evidence left behind of this ice that is the most distinctive feature of the landscape. As illustrated, these 14 areas cover 12 counties (11) stretching from Sligo in the south-west to Antrim in the north-east and together they span across some 1,700,000,000 years of Earth history!

10- A map showing the 14 landscape-based areas that are used in this book to guide us along our "Story Through Time".

11 - The twelve northern counties of Ireland

13

Ox Mountains

In the beginning...

Tucked away in the south-west corner of the region lie the Ox Mountains. Stretching through western County Sligo in a broad band from Lough Talt to Ballysadare and continuing northwards in a narrow arc around Lough Gill and on towards Manorhamilton in Co. Leitrim, this rugged and desolate range of hills contains some of the oldest rocks in the region (12). As such they mark the beginning of our "Story Through Time".

The north-eastern Ox Mountains are mostly composed of a metamorphic rock called gneiss. This rock was originally a sedimentary rock that was deposited as sand in a shallow sea perhaps as long ago as 1,700 million years. It is believed that, at that time, Ireland was part of a single European / North American continent and lay, submerged below a shallow sea, possibly somewhere close to the southern polar regions. At that time the sea was filled with only very primitive forms of life while any land was totally barren of life. Sometime around 1000 million years ago these rocks were caught up in a major mountain building event resulting from the collision of continents. During the early part of this collision event, some intrusive igneous rocks called tonalite and gabbro were intruded into the sandstones. The collision also pushed the original sandstones deep down into the Earth's crust, possibly as deep as 45km. There the sandstones, which had now been metamorphosed to gneiss, became interleaved with material from the Earth's mantle which is now preserved as the strange, dark green rock serpentinite. This great collision created a single, large supercontinent on the Earth that has been given the name Rodinia. By 900 million years ago Rodinia was surrounded by a single ocean.

However, nature had not finished with the gneiss, tonalite and gabbros of the Ox Mountains. By 850 million years ago, the supercontinent Rodinia had begun to split up. One portion of Rodinia became

12- The Ox Mountains

unstable and began to fragment as a new ocean developed. New, smaller continents were created as this ocean widened with the newly formed continents of Laurentia (eastern North America, northern Europe and Siberia) moving apart from Gondwana (Africa, southern Europe, India, Antarctica and Australasia). This split also affected the area we know today as Ireland. The northern half of Ireland remained as part of Laurentia while the southern half formed part of the small continent of Avalonia which had broken away from Gondwana (13). The two halves of Ireland became separated by the ever-widening Iapetus Ocean *(in Greek mythology Iapetus was the father of Atlas after whom the present Atlantic Ocean is named)* as Laurentia and Gondwana moved further apart. Eventually however the Iapetus Ocean stopped widening and, as Laurentia and Gondwana began to move closer again, it started to shrink in size. Some 420 million years ago the two halves of Ireland became joined as the small continents of the Iapetus Ocean such as Avalonia collided with the eastern margin of Laurentia. During this collision the gneisses of the Ox Mountains were again greatly altered or metamorphosed. This time sheets of molten magma forced their way up into the Earth's crust and into the gneiss. This magma cooled to form an intrusive igneous rock called pegmatite (which is a variety of granite).

13 - Earth some 750 million years ago just after the ancient supercontinent of Rodinia began to fragment into the new continents of Laurentia and Gondwana.

Many of these ancient rocks are best seen in the area just south of Lough Gill to the east of Sligo town (12). From the car park on the R287 road just at the southernmost point of Lough Gill follow the footpath north into the forest. Blocks of the grey, white and pink banded gneiss lie beside the path (14). The different colours and layers reflect variations in the content of the different minerals that make up the gneiss. After some 2km the path forks; follow the right hand fork and look for two large exposures of rock on the left. The second exposure has a distinctive 60cm wide sheet of pegmatite cutting vertically across the banding in the gneiss. At the base of this exposure a second sheet of pegmatite was intruded parallel to the banding.

14 - Blocks of colour banded gneiss, alongside the forest path at the southern shore of Lough Gill.

15 - Serpentinite, a rock believed to have been derived from the Earth's mantle, seen here in the Slishwood Gap south of Lough Gill. The hammer shaft is 30cm long.

It is sobering to stop and think of the age of these rocks and the colossal events they have witnessed. Further blocks of gneiss can be seen alongside the path and some of the gneiss shows small contortions, or folding, of the layers. This folding developed very slowly deep in the crust as the original sandstone was metamorphosed during the periods of collision. After a sharp turn, walk downhill and turn left at the junction to return to the car park. The serpentinite, the rock that is derived from the Earth's mantle, is also seen along the R287 road. Here, because the serpentinite has been weakened by earth movements, it now forms a softer rock than gneiss. As such it has been eroded to form the Slishwood Gap. The brown serpentinite reveals a blackish-green colour when broken and can be seen alongside a farm-lane on the right-hand side travelling south and 200m before a sharp bend in the road (15). The Ox Mountains continue north-eastwards towards Manorhamilton and their rugged appearance is in sharp contrast to the rolling hills to the east and west that are underlain by younger rocks such as limestone. To the south west the gneiss gives way to other metamorphic rocks such as schist (16). These schists are intruded by igneous rocks such as granite. Similar rocks also make up much of Counties Donegal, Derry and Tyrone and the story of their formation forms the next few chapters in the unfolding tale of our "Landscapes From Stone".

16 - Schist from the Ox Mountains just south of Easky Lough in west Sligo. These schists, together with igneous rocks such as granite, are typical of this part of the Ox Mountains. One Punt coin for scale.

South Donegal

The birth of an ocean

Extending from the tumbling cliffs of Slieve League in the west to the lonely shores of Lough Derg in the east, South Donegal has a wide variety of landscapes (17). However, as with the rest of the county, it is the rugged high ground that dominates the landscape of south Donegal and it is in the rocks of these uplands that we continue the story of our "Landscapes From Stone".

The bleak, lonely countryside around Lough Derg is underlain by ancient rocks of a similar age to those of the Ox Mountains further south. Like the gneiss of the Ox Mountains, the rocks around Lough Derg were caught up in two continental collisions over 1000 and 420 million years ago. Although the rocks were originally deposited as coarse-grained sands on the floor of a shallow sea, because of a difference in the metamorphic history here the rocks are not gneisses but psammites. These psammites can be seen along the R233 Pettigo – Lough Derg road and on the northern side of the R232 Pettigo – Donegal road at the Black Gap. At one period during the long history of this area vast quantities of magma were generated deep within the Earth. Some of this magma reached the surface here and was erupted as lava. Volcanoes were built up and many of the small hills that dot the landscape around Lough Derg represent the deep roots of these volcanoes, aeons of erosion having removed the volcanoes themselves. One such hillock can be seen at Lough Lareen, 1km east of Ballyshannon.

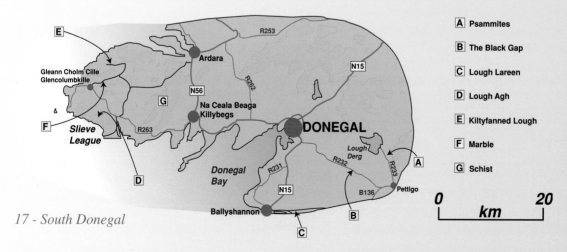

17 - South Donegal

A Psammites

B The Black Gap

C Lough Lareen

D Lough Agh

E Kiltyfanned Lough

F Marble

G Schist

As mentioned earlier, sometime around 850 million years ago the ancient supercontinent of Rodinia began to fragment. As a large portion of Rodinia itself split apart a new shallow sea was formed separating the new continents of

Laurentia and Gondwana. Initially this ancient sea was shallow and as mountain ranges bordering this sea were eroded sediments accumulated on the shallow sea floor eventually creating new sedimentary rocks. These sandstones, limestones and mudstones are, in places, accompanied by a more unusual sedimentary rock called a conglomerate. A conglomerate is a sedimentary rock that contains many stones, pebbles or even boulders of other, older rocks. This particular conglomerate contains pebbles of granite, quartzite (metamorphosed sandstone) and dolomite (a sedimentary rock related to limestone) and can also be found in parts of Connemara, Co. Galway and in Co. Mayo to the south-west and in many parts of Scotland to the north-east. By comparing it to similar rocks forming today, it appears that it formed during an Ice Age that gripped this area some 600 million years ago. At that time the continent of Laurentia, of which

the northern half of Ireland was then a part, lay in high polar latitudes in the southern hemisphere, close to the present position of the Antarctic coastline. We also know that for at least part of that time the climate was cold enough for great ice sheets to develop. As glaciers or ice sheets grow they can pick up large amounts of rock debris which gets deposited when the ice starts to melt. The conglomerate formed in shallow water near an ancient coastline as melting ice shelves or icebergs, which had calved off the main ice sheet, dropped their load of stones and pebbles onto the sea floor.

18 - Kiltyfanned Lough. Quartzite and conglomerate can be seen here; the latter was formed during an Ice Age that gripped this area over 600 mya.

This glacial conglomerate can be seen in several places along the Slieve League peninsula of south-west Donegal. The two best places to see it are just to the south west of Lough Agh on the northern side of Slieve League or at the north side of the road just north of the eastern end of Kiltyfanned Lough which lies to the north-east of Glencolumbkille (Gleann Cholm Cille) (18). Here the rock occurs among hard metamorphic rocks such as schists, marbles and quartzites. These are the altered remains of mudstones, limestones and sandstones that were deposited along with the conglomerate in the ancient sea that covered this area some 600 million years ago. These rocks however do not occur randomly but are arranged in a particular order or sequence. Near Glencolumbkille the rock marble can be found. This marble, seen in scattered outcrops 2km east of Glencolumbkille, was formed as a dolomite in a shallow lagoon. Nearby, the high sea cliffs of Slieve League are mostly formed from the rock quartzite. Quartzite is a metamorphosed sandstone that was deposited in a shallow sea as the ice, of that ancient Ice Age, was retreating (19). Following deposition of this sandstone however, the sea began to deepen and rocks such as mudstones (now metamorphosed to schists) were deposited. These schists form the high ground of Crownarad and Mulnanaff west of Killybegs (Na Ceala Beaga). This same sequence of rocks indicating a general progression to deeper water occurs all over Donegal as well as in Mayo and Scotland. Why?

19 - Quartzite, the hardened sands of an ancient sea floor, now helps to makes up the dramatic sea cliffs of Slieve League. At 595m high, these are the highest cliffs in Ireland.

Because this sequence of rocks can be traced over a great distance, all the rocks have been grouped together and are collectively known as the Dalradian Supergroup *(after the ancient kingdom of Dalriada that straddled both Ireland and Scotland).* Together with the igneous rock granite these Dalradian rocks make up much of the rest of Donegal and indeed much of the adjacent Sperrin Mountains in Counties Derry and Tyrone. After deposition of the early limestones, conglomerate and sandstones, the ancient shallow Dalradian sea began to deepen. This deepening happened as the crust of the Earth became stretched and thinned leading to subsidence of the ocean floor. This stretching was caused as the two continents of Laurentia and Gondwana, which had broken away from Rodinia, drifted further apart. Eventually the floor of the Dalradian sea fractured, or rifted, and as Laurentia and Gondwana drifted further and further apart the new Iapetus Ocean formed between them. This ocean separated the north and west of Ireland which remained part of Laurentia from the south and east of Ireland. It formed part of the small continent of Avalonia which lay between Laurentia and Gondwana.. But the Iapetus Ocean did not go on growing forever. Eventually, plate movements changed and as Iapetus shrunk in size, the two continents of Laurentia (along with northern Ireland) and Gondwana once again got closer and closer together. More significantly Avalonia (Newfoundland, Nova Scotia, southern Ireland and southern Britain) and another small continent called Baltica (Sweden and Finland), were forced into collision with the eastern margin of Laurentia. The forces released as they collided altered the Dalradian sedimentary rocks into metamorphic schists, quartzites and marbles, and folded and faulted them during two episodes of mountain building. Evidence for these events now takes us to North Donegal where we continue our "Story Through Time".

North Donegal

Continental collision and the death of an ocean

T he rugged coastline of North Donegal is pierced in several places by winding inlets of the Atlantic Ocean, such as Lough Swilly, Sheep Haven and Mulroy Bay. These extend inland for many kilometres and separate scenic peninsulas, such as Inis Eoghain (Inishowen), Fanad, Rosguill and Horn Head (20). The inlets were carved by glaciers during the last Ice Age which ended only 13,000 years ago. By contrast, the peninsulas are made up of rocks that are over 600 million years old and which were folded and crumpled several times during a series of great continental collision some 470 - 420 million years ago.

As mentioned previously, most of the rocks of Donegal belong to the Dalradian Supergroup which were deposited as sands, muds and limestones on the floor of an ancient shallow sea before the formation of the Iapetus Ocean. This ocean developed as the ancient continents of Laurentia and Gondwana drifted apart. Eventually however, and following a change in the movement of the Earth's plates, the Iapetus Ocean began to shrink in size as these two continents moved closer together again (21). Starting some 500 million years ago the sediments and rocks of the ocean floor became squeezed as the continents moved closer to each other. This movement forced the small continents of Avalonia and Baltica into collision with the eastern margin of Laurentia. As the various fragments of these continents began their long and complex process of

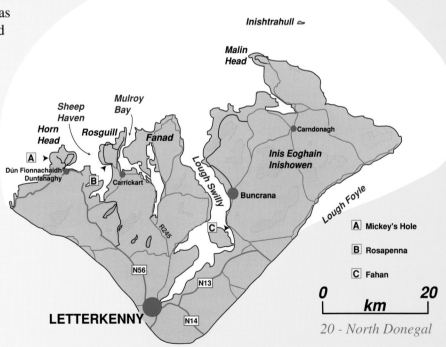

Inishtrahull

Malin Head

Sheep Haven

Mulroy Bay

Horn Head

Rosguill

Fanad

Carndonagh

Inis Eoghain Inishowen

A

Dún Fionnachaidh
Dunfanaghy

B

Carrickart

Lough Swilly

Buncrana

Lough Foyle

R245

C

N56

N13

LETTERKENNY

N14

A Mickey's Hole

B Rosapenna

C Fahan

0   km   20

20 - North Donegal

Continental collision and the death of an ocean

Cambrian 545 - 495 mya

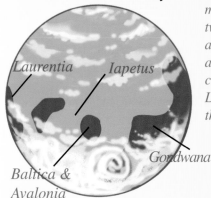

21 - During Cambrian times, over 500 million years ago, Ireland was divided in two with the north and west as part of the ancient continent of Laurentia and the south and east forming part of Avalonia which lay close to the larger continent of Gondwana. Laurentia and Gondwana were separated by the Iapetus Ocean.

Silurian 443 - 417 mya

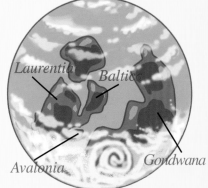

During the Silurian Period the Iapetus Ocean contracted as Laurentia and Gondwana moved closer together. This movement eventually forced the small continents of Avalonia and Baltica into collision with the eastern margin of Laurentia.

collision, the rocks were heated and transformed into the metamorphic quartzites, marbles and schists we see today. Additionally, they were thrust upwards to create a new mountain range, the Caledonian Mountains. These mountains stretched from Norway through Scotland and Ireland and southwards into Newfoundland and Nova Scotia in Canada. At that time, all of these areas formed part of the one continent. At their highest, the Caledonian Mountains are believed to have been higher than the present day Himalayas (**22**). Again, erosion over the vast expanse of geological time has laid bare the roots of this once impressive mountain chain. However, the present day mountains of Norway, the Scottish Highlands, the Donegal and Sperrin Mountains, the mountains of Connemara and the hills of eastern Canada are a testament to the former scale of the Caledonian Mountains and to the forces that created them. It was also this complex series of collisions that finally brought together north-west Ireland and south-east Ireland, welding them together along a line of join, or suture, which runs from Clogherhead in Co. Louth on the east coast to the Shannon Estuary in the south-west (**23**).

Many years of detective work carried out on the rocks of North Donegal by generations of geologists have led to the conclusion that many separate episodes of deformation affected the rocks of this area. Evidence of the great forces released during this period of mountain building can be seen on the shore at Rosapenna at the southern end of Rosguill (**24**). Here beds of sandstone and siltstone have been metamorphosed into quartzites and pelites respectively and folded so that the original horizontal layers of rock (or beds) are now vertical! Elsewhere the forces released during the

23 - *Vertical layers, or beds, of the sedimentary rock greywacke on the shore at Clogherhead, Co. Louth. These rocks contain evidence which suggests that it was here that the two former halves of Ireland were welded, or sutured, together.*

collision were so intense that not only did the rock deform, or fold, but it also fractured and in some instances large volumes of rock were thrust over adjacent layers of rock and transported over some distance. Evidence of one of these dramatic events may be seen on the west coast of Horn Head in the cliffs at Micky's Hole just opposite Harvey's Rocks. Here, finely layered (or cleaved) pelite now lies directly on lighter coloured and finely cleaved quartzite. The boundary between these rock types marks the layer upon which the rocks moved, or slid, and is known to geologists as the Horn Head Slide (25). Further east, on the foreshore at Fahan on the west coast of Inis Eoghain, are psammites and slates that represent the metamorphosed coarse-sandstones and mudstones of the deep ocean floor. Along the loughshore, south-east from Fahan Pier, finely bedded and cleaved slate may be seen while just to the north-west of the pier in a cliff, the slates are clearly deformed, or folded.

The peninsula of Inis Eoghain has some of the most scenic landscapes in Donegal. A drive along the beautiful "Inis Eoghain 100" will take you past many exposures of these metamorphosed, folded and fractured Dalradian rocks. From Malin Head, the most northerly point of the Irish mainland, the view north across the sea leads to the lonely rocks and islets of Inishtrahull. These battered rocks do not belong to the Dalradian Supergroup. Indeed they were already very ancient when the sands and muds of the Dalradian rocks were being deposited. In fact, at 1780 million years old these are the oldest rocks in Ireland. They are mostly formed from an intrusive igneous rock called syenite and are believed to have formed deep in the Earth's crust below a chain of volcanic islands

24 - *Gentle folding developed in vertical layers, or beds, of pelite along the shore at Rosapenna on the south-western side of the Rosguill peninsula. This folding and tilting developed as a response to the high pressures this rock experienced during periods of continental collision.*

22

Continental collision

22 - The collisions of the small continents of Avalonia and Baltica with the eastern margins of Laurentia over 430 million years ago, not only resulted in the closure of the Iapetus Ocean but also in the formation of a new mountain range. This new range of mountains extended from Norway south-west through northern Scotland and into north-west Ireland. They also extended further south-west into Newfoundland and Nova Scotia in eastern Canada as the present day Atlantic Ocean did not exist at that time. At the time of their formation these mountains, called the Caledonians, are believed to have been higher than the present day Himalayas. Millions of years of erosion has greatly reduced the height of this once mighty range and the eroded core of the Caledonians now make up not only the present day mountains of Norway and the Scottish Highlands but also the Sperrin Mountains of Derry and Tyrone, the highlands of Donegal and the mountains of Mayo and Connemara to the south-west.

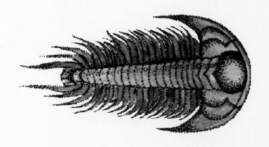

Continental collision and the death of an ocean

somewhat similar to the present day volcanic island chains of the Caribbean or the Pacific. Although similar rocks are found today in southern Greenland, northeastern Canada and southern Scandinavia, 1780 million years ago, they all formed part of the one island chain. The formation of igneous rocks was also a feature of Dalradian times. One need hardly be surprised that the heat generated by the collision of continents caused rocks to melt at depth in the Earth's crust. The story of this igneous activity can be read in rocks right across County Donegal. However, it is to the Donegal Highlands that we now turn to continue our story.

25 - Views of Horn Head form the stunning climax to the scenic Atlantic Drive north from Dunfanaghy.

Pelite

Horn Head Slide

Quartzite

On the western coast of the Horn Head peninsula, at a place named Micky's Hole, the consequences of continental collision become obvious. Here, older dark coloured pelite rests directly on younger, lighter coloured quartzite. The boundary between these rock types is known to geologists as the Horn Head Slide and marks the plane along which the older rocks were thrust over the younger rocks during episodes of continental collision.

Donegal Highlands

Rocks from the furnace

The closure of the ancient Iapetus Ocean was a very long affair. By the end of the Cambrian Period, 545 million years ago, the Iapetus had reached its maximum size and had started to contract. During the following Ordovician Period (495 – 443 million years ago), the ocean contracted and the Caledonian Mountains formed as a complex series of continental collisions occurred. By 430 million years ago, in early Silurian times, the continents had fused together and the Iapetus Ocean was consigned to geological history. While the Dalradian sedimentary rocks were metamorphosed, deformed and fractured by the forces released during these collisions, heat was being generated deep in the Earth's crust. Large volumes of rock were being melted generating vast quantities of molten magma. Between 420 and 390 million years ago, deep below the newly formed Caledonian Mountains of north-west Ireland, this magma began to move upward through large fractures, or faults. As the magma rose up through the crust it cooled and eventually came to rest. Although still below the surface, the magma began to solidify, or crystallise, forming large bodies, or plutons, of intrusive igneous rock. Over the following 390 million years since their formation the overlying Caledonian Mountains have been eroded away exposing the roots of the original mountains. These roots now form the mountains we see today that make up the Donegal Highlands (26). They include not only the

Toraigh
Tory

Ceann Fhanaide
Fanad Head

C

Rosguill

B

Fanad

Inis Bó Finne
Inishbofin

Cnoc Fola
Bloody Foreland

R257

N56

R245

R246

Glen
Lough

A

An Bun Beag
Bunbeg

E

R251

Arainn Mhór
Aran

Anagaire
Annagary

D

Derryveagh Mountains

R259

Loch an Iuír
Lochanure

An Clochán Liath
Dunglow

R254

R250

LETTERKENNY

Gweebarra
Bay

N13

A Mullaghderg

R261

R252

B Doagh Bay

C Melmore

R253

Ballybofey

D Poisoned Glen

N56

N15

E Glenveagh

Ardara

G

F

F Barnesmmore

G Lough Belshade

0   20
km

26 - Donegal Highlands

26

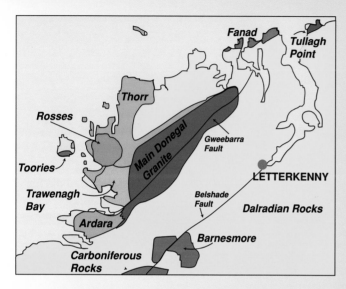

27 - A map showing the location of the Donegal granites

metamorphosed Dalradian rocks but also the plutons of igneous rock that formed deep in the Earth's crust. These rocks are mostly granite and are found scattered across all of County Donegal (27). The granite plutons vary in size and shape with the Derryveagh Mountains in the Donegal Highlands lying at the core of the largest individual granite body.

A total of nine distinct bodies of granite are recognised in Donegal and although geologists have not yet fully worked out the sequence in which the granites were intruded it is considered that the Thorr , Fanad and Tullagh Point granites are the oldest. That portion of the Main Donegal granite lying south-east of the Gweebarra Fault is considered to have been intruded next followed by the Toories and Ardara granites. These were then followed by the Rosses granite and the remaining portion of the Main Donegal granite and finally by the Trawenagh Bay granite.

Extending from Maghery in the south northwards through Bunbeg and Derrybeg to Bloody Foreland, the Thorr granite of north-west Donegal can be seen on the many beaches along this stretch of coast. It also extends some distance offshore and forms the western end of Inishbofin Island (Inis Bó Finne) as well as all but the eastern end of Tory Island (Toraigh). Back on the mainland, on one beach, at Mullaghderg an unusual variety of this granite, referred to as orbicular granite, can be seen. Here small rounded patterns are seen in the granite and they are believed to have formed within the magma as it cooled (28). Although most of the Fanad Granite lies under the sea its southern margins may be seen on the northern ends of both the Rosguill and Fanad peninsulas of North Donegal. The pink coloured granite is obvious at Fanad Head (Ceann Fhionnaide) while on Rosguill the granite is whitish in colour. Here, the rocks provide evidence of what was happening as the granite magmas rose closer to the surface. As the magma rose, the surrounding rocks became fractured and in some instances the magma moved into and filled these fractures, cooling there. At Doagh Bay and at the southern end of Tranafaughboy strand at Melmore, examples can be seen where the granite and the surrounding rock are intimately mixed together (29). These unusual rocks are called migmatites.

28 - Rocks on Mullaghderg Strand near Carrickfin Airport are made of the Thorr Granite. Some of the granite here contains a rounded, or orbicular, texture which formed as the granite magma cooled. Hammer shaft is 30cm long and the granite orb is approximately 10cm across.

Both the Rosses granite and the Ardara granite bodies are roughly circular in shape and while the Ardara granite was intruded into Dalradian rocks, the Rosses granite was intruded into the older Thorr granite. The Rosses granite underlies the wide expanse of flat-lying land between Anagry (Anagaire) and Dunglow (An Clochán Liath). Travelling along the N56 road between Lochanure (Loch an Iuír) and Dunglow, the wet granite can often be seen glistening in the sunlight. However it is the Main Donegal Granite that dominates the Donegal Highlands. Stretching from Glen Lough south-westwards to Gweebarra Bay, it is this granite that gives rise to the magnificent Derryveagh Mountains. The granite mountains have been deeply eroded by the action of ice during the last Ice Age and evidence of this can be seen most dramatically at the Poisoned Glen in Gweedore (Gaoth Dobhair) and in Glenveagh National Park (30). At the Poisoned Glen the ice has created a beautiful U-shaped glaciated valley and while a similar U-shaped valley has been carved out of the granite at Glenveagh here the setting has been added to by the deep waters of Lough Beagh. While both these locations provide ample opportunity to examine the granite, it is probably easier to examine it

29 - Tranafuaghboy Strand at Melmore, near the northern tip of the Rosguill peninsula. Here the local rock was fractured as the granite magma rose into it. The rising magma filled in these cracks where it then cooled. These unusual rocks are called migmatites. Similar rocks can be seen further south on Rosguill at Doagh Bay. Lens cap is 6cm across.

within the grounds of the National Park at Glenveagh. To the south-east the Barnesmore granite forms the dramatic backdrop to the Barnesmore Gap through which the N15 road between Donegal Town and Ballybofey runs (31). The gap, and the road, follow the line of a major geological fault, one of several which cut across the granite body.

As all of these granites were forming, the molten magma heated the adjacent rock into which it was moving. In places this heating was so intense that the adjacent rocks became metamorphosed from their contact with the magma. The greater the distance from the granite contact, the less the rocks were altered. The zone of alteration, or aureole, surrounding the granites differs from one granite to the other but in the case of the Main Donegal Granite it is up to 3km wide in places.

Further chapters of the story of the Iapetus Ocean, its closure and the creation of the Caledonian Mountains can be read in the rocks of the Sperrin Mountains, north-east County Antrim and the Drumlin Belt. There are volcanic rocks in parts of County Tyrone indicating that some magma did reach the surface during the closure of the Iapetus, erupting as lava from volcanoes. These were associated with an arc of volcanic islands that developed as the northern margin of the Iapetus Ocean was subducted. The rocks of the Ards and Lecale peninsulas in County Down were formed in the deep waters of the Iapetus Ocean before it closed and they contain fossil evidence of some of the primitive life that swam in the waters of this vanished sea. However, the present landscape of both these regions owes much of its

30 - The spectacular Poisoned Glen in the heart of the Donegal Highlands. Here, during the last Ice Age, glaciers cut deep into the Main Donegal Granite to create a beautiful u-shaped valley. Incidentally, the glen takes its somewhat ominous name from a poisonous variety of spurge which grows on the valley floor.

character to that most recent of geological events, the Ice Age, and so the landscape and rocks of these regions will be described later.

31 - Lough Belshade lies hidden in the Blue Stack Mountains just north of the Barnesmore Gap. The hills here, on all but the southern side of the lough, are composed of Barnesmore granite. The granite is well exposed and can be seen laid bare on the hillsides.

Clogher Valley

The wearing down of a mountain range

By early Devonian times, 400 million years ago, the newly formed Caledonian Mountains dominated the landscape of Ireland (32). At that time Ireland lay close to the south eastern edge of the newly enlarged continent of Laurentia in the southern tropics, similar in latitude to present day Zimbabwe (33). The high Caledonian Mountains cut off the rain-bearing winds allowing a hot, arid climate to take hold. The newly formed mountains however were very quickly being eroded away and vast quantities of sediment were deposited on the low lying desert plains to the south east of the mountains. This sediment was carried down from the mountains by fast flowing rivers created by flash floods, a scene very typical of arid regions today. Much of this material was in the form of large clasts or boulders of rock as the fast flowing rivers had no time to separate out the fine material from the coarse. Over time, this debris formed the sedimentary rock conglomerate. Conglomerates of this age are found in several parts of northern Ireland, notably in the hills along the northern side of the Clogher Valley in County Tyrone. However it is to the Antrim Coast and Glens that we briefly move to continue our "Story Through Time" (34).

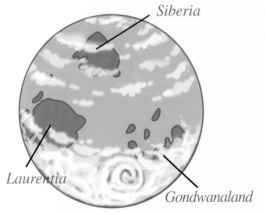

33 - Earth during the Devonian Period, 417 - 354 million years ago. During that time Ireland lay in the southern tropics and, for at least some of that time, experienced an arid climate.

Along the coast between the small villages of Cushendun and Cushendall in the Glens of Antrim are spectacular exposures of the sedimentary rocks conglomerate, sandstone and mudstone (35). From the Bay Hotel in Cushendun a path follows the coast around to some caves. The rock making up the caves and the sea stacks here is mostly conglomerate with some thin layers, or beds, of sandstone and mudstone. Some of the mudstone shows cracks which have been filled in with sandstone. These are fossil mud cracks and they formed just as mud cracks form today – by the drying out of wet mud or clay in the sun. They also confirm the hot, arid climate of Devonian times. At nearby Port Obe, on the coast just north of Cushendall, is another conglomerate. Here many of the boulders and clasts that help make up the conglomerate are of volcanic rock. Additionally, by closely studying the layering (or bedding) in the rocks here, geologists have deduced that the clasts were moved into this area from the south. The conclusion is that these conglomerates did not originate from the Caledonian Mountains to the north and west but from a volcano that lay to the south. However, no further evidence of this volcano exists and its precise location remains unknown. Just south, on the coast

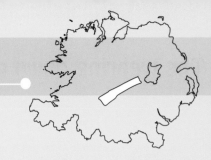

34 - Clogher Valley

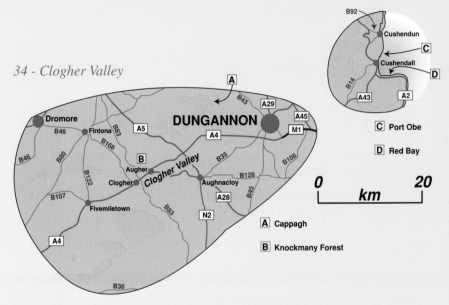

DUNGANNON

Dromore · B46 · Fintona · B863 · A5 · B168 · B80 · B46 · B122 · Augher · Clogher · Clogher Valley · B107 · Fivemiletown · B128 · Aughnacloy · A28 · B45 · B83 · N2 · A4 · B36 · A43 · B106 · B35 · A4 · A29 · A45 · M1 · B92

A · B43

A Cappagh

B Knockmany Forest

Cushendun
C Port Obe
Cushendall
D Red Bay

C Port Obe

D Red Bay

0 km 20

around Red Bay, are more examples of conglomerates, sandstones and mudstones (again with mud-cracks!). Although these rocks also formed in a desert-like climate with flash-floods, the precise age of these rocks is unknown (36). While it is certainly possible that they too are Devonian they may be much younger and date from Permian or Triassic times, 290 - 205 million years ago, when this part of Ireland again experienced a desert climate. The absence of fossils or rocks with radioactive constituents has meant

geologists have, as yet, been unable to provide the answer to this riddle!

Similar sedimentary rocks are found in the hills that line the northern side of the Clogher Valley in County Tyrone (37). Conglomerates make up the hills that run from Cappagh to Knockmany Forest just north of Clogher. The clasts within the conglomerates are again mostly volcanic

35- Here at Cushendun, the conglomerate, sandstone and mudstone that make up the cliffs and sea-stacks were formed during Devonian times when this area of north-east Antrin was experiencing a hot, arid climate. Evidence of this climate comes from the presence of mud-cracks that are seen in some of the mudstone. Hammer shaft is 30cm long for scale.

The wearing down of a mountain range

32 - Ireland during Devonian times formed part of the enlarged continent of Laurentia and, for at least part of the time, experienced a hot, arid climate. The newly formed Caledonian Mountains lay across the north-west of Ireland and continued north-east into Scotland and Norway and also to the south-west into present day Newfoundland and Nova Scotia. A desert plain lay to the south-east of these mountains and as the mountains were being eroded, flash-floods brought down large amounts of sediment from thehighlands and built large outwash plains out onto the desert floor. Sediment was also derived from volcanic rocks somewhere to the south although no remains of these former volcanoes are seen today. The compacted desert sediments eventually formed conglomerates, sandstones and mudstones which can be seen today in the hills along the northern side of the Clogher Valley and further to the north-east near Cushendun. Co. Antrim.

During the Devonian, many varieties of fish, including sharks, evolved and multiplied in the seas. The colonisation of the land by vegetation, that had commenced during the Silurian Period, proceeded apace during the Devonian and by the end of the Devonian Period dense forest covered vast areas of the continents. It was also during the Devonian that the first tetrapods, or four-legged animals, crawled out of the sea and onto the land. These early amphibians (such as Ichthyostega, pictured below) are believed to have evolved from a type of lungfish and, just as with modern day amphibians, they had to return to water to lay their eggs. The fossil trackway of one of these Devonian amphibians was recently found in rocks in County Kerry.

33

The wearing down of a mountain range

36 - The rocks making up the cliff and also found on the shore here at Red Bay, Co. Antrim are similar to the rocks further north at Cushendun. However it is considered that these Red Bay mudstones, sandstones and conglomerates are younger than those to the north and are probably Triassic in age rather than Devonian.

in origin and in fact some thin flows of lava are also found between beds of conglomerate. As with the conglomerates in north-east Antrim at Port Obe, it is believed that it was erosion of these Clogher Valley volcanoes under arid conditions that gave rise to the conglomerates rather than erosion of the Caledonian Mountains to the north-west. The lavas here are important as they contain radioactive constituents that have allowed geologists to date precisely when they were erupted. The lavas tell us that volcanic activity occurred here some 375 million years ago, two thirds of the way through the Devonian Period. Why volcanoes were erupting at that time in the Clogher Valley remains a mystery.

Further west in the small town of Dromore, Devonian sandstones and mudstones may be seen along the road side below the ruins of the old church (38). These reddish-brown rocks provide further evidence of the existence of the Devonian desert in which they were formed. Some of the thin layers of mudstone show mud-cracks and a few also show fossil ripple-marks,

37 - The Clogher Valley of County Tyrone. The hills on the northern side of the valley are made up of conglomerates which were derived, not from the erosion of the Caledonian Mountains, but from the erosion of volcanoes that existed here during Devonian times. Flows of lava from these volcanoes are also found in the hills here.

38 - The rocks upon which the old church at Dromore, Co. Tyrone, was built include mudstones which show fossilised ripple-marks. These marks indicate the presence of a short-lived desert lake in this area at the time the mudstones were formed. Hammer shaft is 30cm long for scale.

somewhat similar to those seen on a sandy beach. The mudstone (and the ripples) formed in a shallow lake that may have been left behind in the desert after a torrential downpour (again, typical of deserts today). The presence of mud cracks indicates that the lake was short lived and quickly evaporated in the desert heat. The fact that the sandstones and mudstones are fine grained together with the absence of conglomerates in this area indicate that the sediment was deposited far from its source. Similar sandstones and mudstones are found a few kilometres north-west of Dromore. Here microscopic fossils have been found in the rock indicating that these rocks are of a very similar age to the conglomerates of the Clogher Valley.

The Devonian Period saw major evolutionary advances in the development of life on Earth. Some 420 million years ago, during Silurian times, the first plants began to colonise the land. They were followed several million years later, at the dawn of the Devonian period, by animals. At this time many different types of fish evolved in the seas of the Devonian world and it was from a variety of lungfish that the first animal able to walk on land evolved. These first land animals were amphibians but, as they relied on water for reproduction, they could not live totally on land. It would be another 80 million years before the first true land-based animals, the early reptiles, would appear. Plants also flourished during Devonian times and by the close of Devonian times, 354 million years ago, forests had already colonised parts of the Earth. There is no evidence of this explosion of life in this region, although the fossil trackway of one of the early amphibians has been found in Devonian rocks far to the south in County Kerry. The desert climate experienced in this region was hostile to most plant and animal life, just as it is today. However 355 million years ago, the low-lying Devonian desert began to be engulfed by the warm waters of an encroaching sea. Within this sea lived many types of fish, coral, and shelled animals. The remains of these creatures were to become preserved and fossilised in the sediment of the sea floor. It is the story of this sea that now leads us to the Erne Lakelands and West Breifne for our continuing story in stone.

Erne Lakelands

The drowning of the desert

By the end of Devonian times 354 million years ago a warm sea had already covered south-eastern Ireland and was slowly but surely moving north westwards, drowning the landscape as it advanced. At the start of the Carboniferous Period (354 – 290 million years ago) Ireland still belonged to the continent of Laurentia but had moved north and now lay close to or just slightly south of the equator (39). The Caledonian Mountains were now much reduced in height and much of Ireland consisted of a low-lying desert plain. The history of the Carboniferous period in this part of Ireland is the story of the battle between the sea and dry land as the waters of the Carboniferous Ocean were to advance and retreat many times over the coming 64 million years. The story of this struggle begins in the gentle countryside of the Erne Lakelands for it is here that the first pages in the story of the Carboniferous of the region can be read (40).

The waters of the Erne Lakelands are underlain for the most part by rocks that date from the early part of the Carboniferous Period when the sea first advanced over this area. These oldest Carboniferous rocks comprise conglomerates and red sandstones but these quickly change to siltstones and greenish sandstones. More significantly these siltstones and green sandstones contain the fossils of animals that lived in the advancing waters of the warm Carboniferous sea. The sequence of sedimentary rocks seen in parts of the bed of the Cole Bridge River, north of Fivemiletown, indicate that this area lay along the tidal, or shoreline, zone of the Carboniferous sea. With further advances of the sea the rock type being formed changed to limestone, another sedimentary rock. Limestone typically forms in shallow water and often contains abundant fossil remains of the plants and animals that lived in that sea. Along the southern shore of Lower Lough Erne, at Carrickreagh Wood, there are large quarries where this limestone was extracted in the past (41). In some of the layers are the remains of shelled animals such as brachiopods (similar to molluscs), corals and rare examples of sea lily-like creatures called crinoids. These rocks also contain microscopic fossils that have allowed geologists to date these rocks to early Carboniferous times.

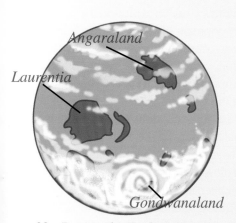

39 - During the Carboniferous Period, Ireland still formed part of the Laurentian continent and straddled the equator.

Although limestone is a sedimentary rock it does not always form solely by deposition of sediment in the same way as conglomerates, sandstones or mudstone. Instead it can also partially form by chemical deposition. If water

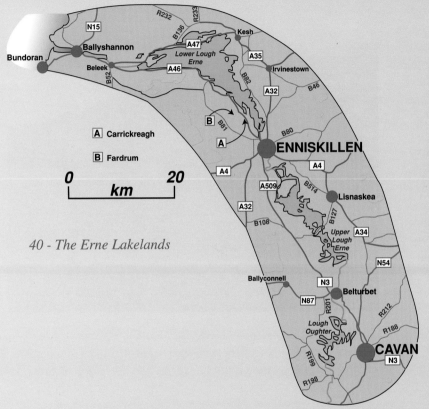

A Carrickreagh

B Fardrum

0   **km**   20

40 - The Erne Lakelands

contains more of a chemical compound called calcium carbonate than it can dissolve, the mineral calcite will form. Calcite makes up the shells of many animals (and part of our own bones) and when these animals die their remains accumulate on the sea floor as a calcareous sediment which later hardens into limestone. Limestone differs from other rocks in that it can be dissolved by ordinary rain water! Although this process is a slow one, over thousands of years large caves can be excavated in limestone often with magnificent stalactites and stalagmites. The limestone along the shores of Lough Erne has been subject to this slow erosive process. In the hills above Ely Forest, just off the A36 road between Enniskillen and Ballyshannon, are three small lakes which are all underlain by limestone. The largest of these lakes is Fardrum Lough but the two smaller lakes, one to the north and one to the south show unusual behaviour related to the limestone. During periods of dry weather these small lakes gradually dry up even though they are not drained by any river. This can even happen during dry weather in the winter and so it is not related to evaporation during a warm summer. It appears that rainwater has attacked the limestone, creating and widening fractures within it and through which the water can slowly seep away. Such lakes, or turloughs, quickly fill up again during wet weather. Elsewhere in Fermanagh rainwater has created even more spectacular features within limestone (see West Breifne). After the deposition of the limestone, earth movements to the north raised the height of the Caledonian Mountains again and led to an increased amount of mud being brought down into the sea. The increased amount of mud being deposited on the sea floor resulted in the rock type being formed changing from limestone to mudstone. This mudstone contains many fossils which are probably most easily seen in the rocks and cliffs at Bundoran in County Donegal. Here abundant shelled brachiopods, corals and crinoids are found, as are the fossil traces of animals that would have burrowed into the muddy floor of the ancient sea. As large sediment-laden rivers drained the Caledonian highlands to the north and west, carrying their debris out into the Carboniferous sea, they began to build deltas out into the water. These deltas however were soon submerged as the sea advanced northwards once more. This emergence and submergence of the land happened several times during the Carboniferous and it is this continuing battle between land and sea that now takes us to West Breifne where the remaining story of the Carboniferous unfolds.

41 - A limestone quarry at Carrickreagh, Co. Fermanagh. Limestone is a sedimentary rock that is composed of the mineral calcite. Calcite is common in the shells and skeletons of many animals and it is quite common to find their fossilised remains within the rock.

Sea and land at war!

Breifne is the ancient name for that region of Ireland which today covers parts of Counties Sligo, Leitrim, Fermanagh, Cavan and Monaghan. The rocks of West Breifne hold the evidence of the struggle between land and sea that took place in this area during the early Carboniferous Period some 330 million years ago (42). At this time, a warm sea had moved up from the south to cover most of this area. At the same time, earth movements to the north had elevated the Caledonian Mountains again and as rivers eroded these highlands, they also carried the eroded sediment out to sea where it was deposited. The rock being formed on the sea bed gradually changed from limestone to mudstone. An increase in the amount of sand being deposited in the sea by these rivers resulted in a shallowing of the sea as deltas began to form, allowing the development of sandstone. Eventually the delta top would build up sufficiently to form dry land. The first delta to develop in this area of north-west Ireland was soon drowned as the sea re-advanced northwards. This sea was warm and clear as Ireland at that time lay close to the equator and basked in a climate not unlike that enjoyed today by the Bahama Islands. The sea swarmed with life and banks of lime-rich mud accumulated on the sea bed to form limestone (43). As these mudbanks eventually came close to sea level corals colonised their tops to form coral reefs. At this stage however the deltas returned. In total, geologists have recognised three main episodes of delta formation here, all identified by the presence of large units of sandstone. On some occasions when the tops of the deltas formed dry land, the sands and muds would dry out and mudcracks would

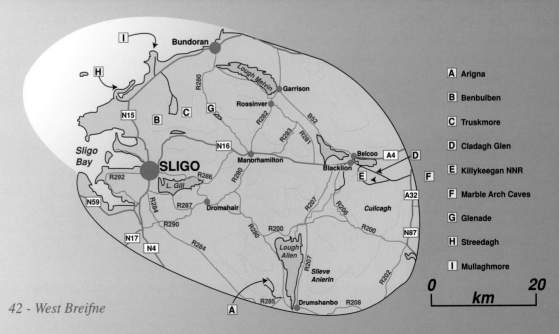

42 - West Breifne

A Arigna

B Benbulben

C Truskmore

D Cladagh Glen

E Killykeegan NNR

F Marble Arch Caves

G Glenade

H Streedagh

I Mullaghmore

Sea and land at war!

43 - For much of the Carboniferous Period from 354 - 290 million years ago, Ireland lay submerged below the warm waters of a tropical sea. This sea swarmed with life and the fossilised remains of many of the plants and animals that thrived in the warm waters are preserved today in the limestones, mudstones and sandstones that formed during this time. Coral reefs (1) were common and many shelled animals such as brachiopods, bivlaves (2) and ammonoids (3) swam in the warm waters or moved along the sea bed looking for food. Strange sea lily-like creatures called crinoids (4) were very common, growing up from the sea bed by means of a long stalk from which tentacle-like arms would have swayed in the currents again looking for food In addition to these groups, fish were very common and many varieties of shark evolved (5).

On land, all the major groups of plants, except flowering plants, had appeared and great swampy forests developed. These forests became the source of the great coal deposits that were to help power the industrial development of the 19th century. Amphibians were the dominant group of tetrapods although the first groups of reptiles appeared during the Carboniferous. Insects were very common as the Carboniferous swamps provided an ideal environment for them. Among the insects that appeared at this time were dragonflies with wingspans over 50cm and cockroaches over 10cm long!

form. There is also evidence of salts such as gypsum which formed as lakes or lagoons evaporated in the heat. Just as with modern day deltas, such as those of the Nile and Mississippi Rivers, the tops of the deltas became thickly vegetated and swamps developed. As the trees and plants of these forests died they decayed slowly and, over time, coal developed. Some of these coal seams, such as those around Arigna and Slieve Anierin on either side of Lough Allen, have been mined. As coal is buried it changes its structure. The different types of coal that develop during burial therefore help indicate the depth to which the coal has been buried. We know from the type of coal present in this area that it must have been buried to a depth of some 4km! Erosion has since removed all this overlying sediment indicating that the struggle between land and sea continued long after the formation of the rocks we now see today.

No major earth movements have affected this area since the deposition of the rocks of the Carboniferous. No mountain building has occurred in north-west Ireland since then and the rocks today form the same layers they did when they were formed. This layering has given rise to the characteristic profile of the mountains of West Breifne. From Cuilcagh and Slieve Anierin in the east to Benbulben and Truskmore in the west, the mountains all take on a table-like shape (44). In the case of Cuilcagh it is the hard sandstone from one of the deltas that forms the protective cap to the mountain, preventing the underlying mudstones and limestones from being eroded away. On Benbulben most of the sandstone has now been eroded allowing the underlying limestone to form the steep and dramatic cliffs that dominate the landscape of Yeats Country.

On the north side of Cuilcagh, the limestone has been attacked by rainwater allowing the formation of some beautiful karst scenery. Karst is the collective name given to limestone features created by the dissolution of the rock by rainwater (45). These

44 - The magnificent mountain of Benbulben rises steeply from the farmland north of Sligo town. Its table-top shape is characteristic of many of the mountains in West Breifne and is caused by alternating layers of harder and softer rock which offer varying resistence to the agents of erosion. In the case of Benbulben the hard sandstone cap has almost been completely removed exposing the steep cliffs of limestone below. Further east, on Cuilcagh, the hard sandstone cap is still largely intact.

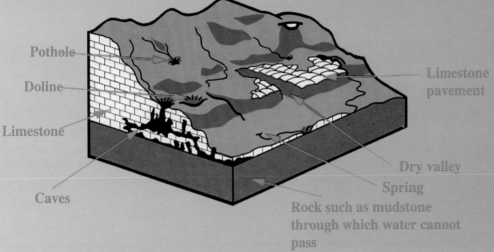

Pothole

Doline

Limestone

Caves

Limestone pavement

Dry valley

Spring

Rock such as mudstone through which water cannot pass

45 - Limestone, unlike most other rocks, is slowly dissolved by natural rainwater. The diagram above illustrates some of the features that can result from this process.

features include springs, such as those along the Cladagh Glen between Blacklion (Co. Cavan) and Florencecourt (Co. Fermanagh) and limestone pavement, such as that at Killykeegan (Marlbank, Co. Fermanagh) or along sections of the waymarked Cavan Way and Ulster Way in this area (46). Undoubtedly the most spectacular karst features of West Breifne are the showcaves at Marble Arch (Marlbank, Co. Fermanagh). Here a guided tour introduces the visitor to the caves and their stalagmites and stalactites as well as explaining how the caves formed (47). Further west, Glenade in Co. Leitrim is floored by soft mudstone. Unprotected by harder sandstone or limestone, the mudstone was easily eroded away when glaciers invaded this valley during the last Ice Age.

Perhaps the best place to see the Carboniferous mudstones, sandstones and limestones of West Breifne is along the coastline between Sligo Town and Mullaghmore Head. At Streedagh Strand (off the main N15 Sligo to Ballyshannon road at Grange), limestones and mudstones can be examined. They are packed with

46 - Limestone pavement along the waymarked Ulster Way above Florencecourt Forest, Co. Fermanagh.

47 - Stalagmites hanging from the ceiling of the Marble Arch Caves in Co. Fermanagh. The caves have been excavated by the Sruh Croppa, Aghinrahan and Owenbrean rivers which sink into the limestone above Marble Arch and emerge below the cave system as a single river, the Cladagh. The stalagmites form as water, rich in the mineral calcite, drips from the ceiling. Every time a drop of water falls, it leaves behind a small piece of calcite which, over tens of thousands of years, builds up into the stalagmites we see today.

the fossils of animals such as corals, brachiopods and crinoids that lived in the warm Carboniferous seas (48). Further north at Mullaghmore, the alternating layers of mudstone and sandstone, typical of the deltaic environments, can be examined (49). Although there are few shelly fossils here, there are many examples of the fossil trails and trackways of the creatures that burrowed into these sediments over 330 million years ago.

Globally, the remainder of Carboniferous times was marked by the great diversity of plant life that evolved. Insects became abundant and dragonflies with 50cm wingspans and cockroaches over 10cm long evolved. Amphibians evolved into true reptiles while sharks and many types of fish swam in the sea. The continents continued their relentless drift across the surface

48 - The rocks at Streedagh Point, Co. Sligo, consist mostly of limestone and mudstone. The rock surfaces, or bedding planes, are in most places covered with fossils, particularly those of large solitary corals such as those pictured here. These fossil corals show a form of banding which is considered to be a result of seasonal variation in the rates of coral growth (somewhat like the annual rings in trees). One punt coin for scale.

49 - Layers, or beds, of sedimentary rock of Carboniferous age at Mullaghmore Head, Co. Sligo. The two thick beds at the top of the cliff are formed of sandstone deposited on the bottom of a river flowing across a delta. The river channel cut down into previously deposited sands and silts which form the lower part of the cliff.

of the Earth. Laurentia, of which Ireland was still a part, began to collide with the continent of Gondwanaland (present day Africa, South America, Antarctica, Australia, India, southern Europe and the Middle East). This collision, which in total was to last from 350 to 250 million years ago, resulted in the formation of the Appalachian Mountains along the eastern seaboard of the USA. Gondwanaland drifted over southern polar regions leading to the creation of a Carboniferous Ice Age. Further north, Kazakhstan and Siberia together formed the continent of Angaraland and it was slowly drifting towards collision with the eastern portion of Laurentia (50). During the Permian period these collisions would lead to the creation of a single supercontinent. They would also mark the dawn of very different environmental and climatic conditions for that part of the world we know today as Ireland. It is in the rocks of the Lagan Valley that evidence of these changes can best be seen.

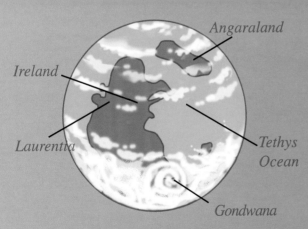

50 - By the close of the Carboniferous Period, 290 million years ago, Angaraland was in collision with eastern Laurentia while Gondwanaland was colliding with southern Laurentia. These collisions would result in the creation of a single supercontinent, Pangea.

Lagan Valley

The deserts return

The collision of the ancient continents of Laurentia and Gondwanaland, towards the end of the Carboniferous Period, resulted in the formation of the Appalachian Mountains of the eastern USA. During the succeeding Permian Period of 290 – 248 million years ago it also created a range of mountains in Europe, the Hercynian Mountains, as various parts of modern day Europe collided with each other. These mountains are now much eroded but their remains are seen in south-west Ireland, Brittany and in the Czech Republic. Furthermore, by 248 million years ago, Angaraland had collided with eastern Laurentia thus completing the formation of a single supercontinent called Pangea which means "all earth". (51). This collision between Angaraland and Laurentia created the Ural Mountains that today straddle the boundary between Europe and Asia. Globally sea levels fell, perhaps by as much as 100m. The ice sheets over the southern polar regions retreated to be replaced by bogs and peat swamps. This great shifting of the Earth's tectonic plates had dramatic consequences for Ireland. The warm seas and swampy deltas of the Carboniferous disappeared as hot desert conditions took hold. Ireland lay deep within the continent of Pangea, probably a few degrees north of the equator. The Hercynian Mountains had cut off any rain-bearing winds and, as temperatures rose, a landscape similar to the rocky deserts of parts of present day Yemen and Saudi Arabia, developed. The landscape of north-east Ireland (52) was generally low and the weathering of exposed rock under the hot, arid climate created a regolith of angular fragments that later became consolidated to form a sedimentary rock called breccia. This Permian breccia can be seen along the southern foreshore of Belfast Lough at Cultra, about 100m east of the junction between the Seafront and Circular Roads. Also along the foreshore at Cultra is a Permian

51 - The Permian world with the single supercontinent of Pangea surrounded by the single ocean of Tethys.

A Cultra

B Scrabo

C Collin Glen

D Belshaw's Quarry

E Carnmoney Hill

52 - The Lagan Valley

limestone. This limestone contains a high content of the mineral magnesium, is a pale yellow colour and contains abundant shelly fossils of gastropods (whelks) and bivalves (cockles) that lived in the sea. So what were marine animals doing in a supposed hot desert?

During the second half of the Permian period seas advanced over large parts of northern and central Europe. In Ireland a sea moved in from the north and, at times, covered the northern and eastern parts of the country. The Bakevellia Sea was shallow and, as portions of it became isolated, under the hot climate it began to evaporate (53). As it evaporated different minerals and salts were formed, the earliest of which was the magnesium-rich limestone. This limestone has been quarried in the past when it was used as a decorative corner stone by the builders of Carrickfergus Castle on the Co. Antrim side of the lough (54). The Bakevellia Sea retreated at the end of Permian times some 250 million years ago at a time when a major and mysterious catastrophe engulfed the Earth.

The end of the Permian was marked by the biggest extinction of life the planet has yet witnessed. During the Permian Period, reptiles continued to diversify and one branch developed mammal-like characteristics, such as being warm- blooded. They would, in time, evolve into true mammals. Some of these early mammal-like reptiles were carnivorous and were up to 3m long with large sail-like fins on their backs. But at the close of the Permian many groups of plants and animals became extinct. Most of these were marine and one estimate suggests that up to 90% of all species died out in the so-called end Permian mass-extinction. Many theories have been put forward to account for this and other mass-extinctions. Recently the idea of dramatic environmental change brought on as the result of an asteroid or comet impact or of intense volcanic activity has been fashionable and it may well have been one or other of these events that was responsible for the great extinction of life at the end of the Permian. This event was a major watershed in the evolution of life on Earth. It

54 - Carrickfergus Castle, Co. Antrim. When the Normans built this castle in the 12th century they used a light coloured magnesium-rich limestone from across Belfast Lough for the decorative corner stone. This limestone was formed by the evaporation of salt water under a hot, desert like climate which this area experienced during Permian times over 250 million years ago.

The deserts return

53 - *During the Permian Period, 290 - 248 million years ago, Ireland lay in the centre of the supercontinent Pangea, and experienced hot and often desert-like conditions. On occasions arms of the ocean extended into the area only to become isolated from the main body of water and then evaporate away under the hot Permian sun. One such series of incursions happened when the Bakevellia Sea repeatedly invaded from the north, drowning the desert landscape, only to become isolated. As it evaporated, salts were left behind. Further south, the Zechstein Sea repeatedly drowned a vast area of land covering what is now the southern North Sea and across north central Europe into Poland and Belarus. Again vast thicknesses of salt were created. These periods of evaporation continued into the Triassic Period and it is considered that the salt beneath Carrickfergus, Co. Antrim is of this age.*

The Permian Period was the age of the mammal-like reptiles, our own distant ancestors. Although these creatures were reptiles they also had many of the characteristics of present day mammals. These animals were largely unaffected by the great mass-extinction of life at the end of the Permian and towards the end of the Triassic, when they began to decline, some groups evolved into the first true mammals such as Megazostrodon (below). It was also towards the end of the Triassic that a new group of animals evolved from a different group of reptiles. This new group were to become the dominant large life form on Earth for the following 150 million years. They were the dinosaurs!

The deserts return

Ireland

55 - Earth during the Triassic, 248 - 206 million years ago. The supercontinent Pangea was still largely intact but was rotating clockwise. This movement resulted in the continuing northwards drift of Ireland and Britain. By the close of the Triassic the breakup of Pangea had already begun.

marked the end of the Palaeozoic Era and the dawn of the Mesozoic Era, the so-called Age of the Reptiles.

The dawn of the Triassic Period in Ireland (248 – 206 million years ago) saw a return to largely desert conditions. Still as part of the supercontinent Pangea, the region had drifted north to lie in latitudes similar to present day Sudan (55). The climate remained hot and arid with the low-lying plains punctuated by rivers. These rivers carried large amounts of sand which were deposited onto the plains and reworked by the wind into dunes. This sand later compacted into sandstone which can be seen today in the old quarries at Scrabo, just outside Newtownards, Co. Down (56). Some of the layering (or lamination) seen in the sandstone here is typical of layering seen in modern river beds or lakes and the presence of thin seams of mudstone, together with mudcracks, indicate that these bodies of water occasionally dried out. Some of the individual sand grains here are very well rounded and are typical of sand grains weathered by wind. Such processes are typical of arid regions today. Fossils are very rare but the footprint of an early reptile has been found here and can be seen today in the Ulster Museum, Belfast. The sandstones at Scrabo have thick dark bands running

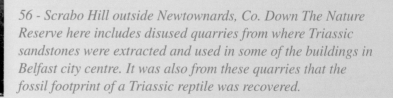

56 - Scrabo Hill outside Newtownards, Co. Down The Nature Reserve here includes disused quarries from where Triassic sandstones were extracted and used in some of the buildings in Belfast city centre. It was also from these quarries that the fossil footprint of a Triassic reptile was recovered.

57 - The salt mines at Carrickfergus have been in use for many years. The photographs above indicate what conditions were like in the mine in the early 20th century. Large thickness of salts accumulated here following the evaporation of large bodies of water during the Triassic Period, some 248 - 206 million years ago.

through them. These are made of the igneous rock dolerite which, as magma, was injected into the sandstone as (vertical) dykes and (horizontal) sills during a period of volcanic activity some 55 – 60 million years ago.

The desert landscapes of north-east Ireland gradually changed during early Triassic times as the sea encroached once more. Lagoons and areas of shallow water developed and, under the hot climate, rates of evaporation were high. Mudstone formed on the floor of these bodies of water and it can be seen today along the Collin Glen in Belfast. Sometimes the water would evaporate away totally and large thicknesses of salts developed. These salts included gypsusm, anhydrite and halite (rocksalt). Below Carrickfergus the rocksalt has been mined for many years (57). Here it is a total of 40m thick but under Larne, to the north-east, it is over 400m thick in total. The gypsum has been mined further south at Kingscourt, Co. Cavan.

The Triassic saw the reptiles become the dominant group of animals on Earth. While some reptiles started on the evolutionary road that was eventually to lead to the appearance of the dinosaurs, other reptiles returned to the sea (eg. the Ichthyosaurs) and others took to the air (e.g. the Pterosaurs). The first true mammals appeared (e.g. the shrew-like *Megazostrodon*) and in the sea fish, which were little affected by the Permian extinction, continued to thrive. Towards the end of the Triassic Period a major advance of the sea occurred in Ireland. This was to herald the marine conditions that were to prevail here throughout the early part of the succeeding Jurassic Period. The sediments deposited on the floor of this sea, together with their fossils, are today preserved at the foot of the cliffs along the Antrim Coast Road. It is therefore to the Antrim Coast and Glens that we now move to continue our Story Through Time.

Jurassic Park!

At the close of the Triassic Period some 206 million years ago, the supercontinent of Pangea, of which Ireland was still a part, began to fragment. This breakup began with the eruption of lava along a fracture, or rift, that developed between present day North America and north-west Africa. This rifting would eventually lead to the creation of a new ocean, the Atlantic. Further south, small fragments began to break away

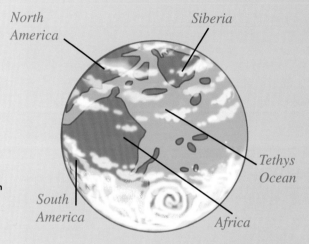

58 - *During the Jurassic period the fragmentation of Pangea continued and the continents we are familiar with today gradually began to take shape.*

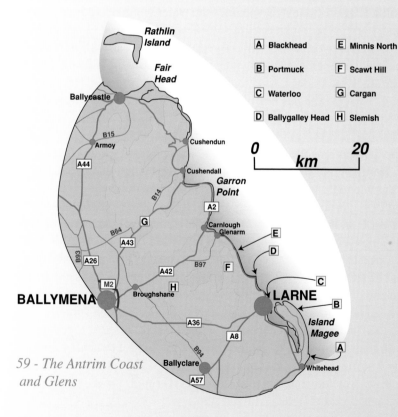

A	Blackhead	E	Minnis North
B	Portmuck	F	Scawt Hill
C	Waterloo	G	Cargan
D	Ballygalley Head	H	Slemish

59 - The Antrim Coast and Glens

from the eastern edge of the former continent of Gondwana, drifting northwards (58). In northern Ireland the start of the Jurassic Period (206 – 142 million years ago) saw most of the land submerged by a shallow sea. Any remaining areas of land would have enjoyed a warm, wet climate with lush vegetation. Dinosaurs such as *Stegosaurus, Diplodocus* or *Megalosaurus* may have roamed land areas at this time but erosion has removed any evidence of their former existence. Mud collecting on the floor of this

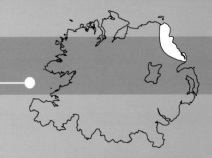

early Jurassic sea compacted into mudstone. The sea however was very rich in marine life and the mudstone not only contains some thin beds of limestone but also the fossil remains of many of these creatures. Evidence of this can be seen in the rocks of the Antrim Coast and Glens (59). Jurassic mudstones can be examined on the foreshore at Waterloo Cottages, on the coast road just north of Larne (60). Here the fossils include bivalves (cockles) and the now extinct nautilus-like ammonites. Further north along the coast at Garron Point, fragments from the backbone of a large marine reptile were found several years ago. Unfortunately a car park now covers this site and the possibility of further reptile finds has been removed. The Jurassic mudstone of the Antrim coast is impermeable, that is it does not allow water to pass through it into the rocks below. Consequently, in times of heavy rainfall, any water trickling down through the rocks above becomes trapped in the mudstone which quickly becomes waterlogged. Because of this it becomes unstable and prone to movement. All along the Antrim coast are examples of landslides and mudflows caused either by movement of the Jurassic mudstone after it became waterlogged or by movement

60 - Grey mudstones and limestones of Jurassic age along the foreshore at Waterloo, just north of Larne, Co. Antrim. These rocks, formed as mud on the floor of an ancient sea, were compacted and hardened into rock. Hammer shaft is 30cm long for scale.

as a result of the weight of the overlying rock. The Minnis North mudflow, just south of Ballygalley, is often active after heavy rain and occasionally forces the closure of the Coast Road. The Jurassic mudstone has also been responsible for the spectacular landslips at Garron Point (61). Here, during the last Ice Age, the ice sheet wedged against the coast at this point, holding the cliff upright. As the ice melted however, the support for the cliff was removed and large blocks of rock slipped on the weak mudstone and rotated seawards.

By the close of the Jurassic Period the dinosaurs, which had become the dominant life form on land, were joined in the air by the first birds while mammals remained a small, unimportant group of animals. The Jurassic also saw the continued breakup of Pangea. While Gondwana continued to break up, the first signs of the fragmentation of Laurentia occurred. A rift opened down the line of the North Sea as the North Atlantic Ocean made its first attempt to open. This

Jurassic Park!

61 - Garron Point, Co. Antrim. Here a series of large blocks of white chalk, and overlying dark basalt, have slipped seawards. Weak mudstones of Jurassic age lie below the chalk and these mudstones act as a barrier to water flowing down from above and therefore act as a lubricant. During the last Ice Age, ice banked up against the cliffs here and supported them. But after the ice melted these large blacks slipped on the mudstone below creating the scene we see today.

attempt at the formation of a new ocean however was destined to fail. Many millions of years later however this North Sea rift was to have great economic importance as it marks the site of most of the oil fields of that area. In Ireland, after the deposition of the mudstone in the shallow seas of early Jurassic times, the sea probably retreated and for the rest of the Jurassic Period, Ireland formed a well vegetated landmass. However, any evidence of this time, and consequently any evidence of an Irish Jurassic Park, has been removed by subsequent erosion!

During the early part of the succeeding Cretaceous Period (142 – 65 million years ago), Ireland probably remained a land mass although the sea briefly flooded the south and east Antrim area (62). A green sandstone and mudstone were deposited on the floor of the shallow sea, the green colour coming from the mineral glauconite. The presence of glauconite is important as it only forms in shallow sea water and therefore helps to confirm the environment in which these early Cretaceous rocks formed. These glauconitic rocks are best seen towards the top of

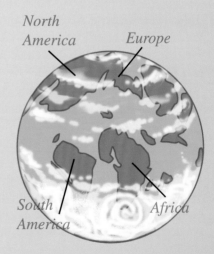

62 - Earth during the Cretaceous. In the northern hemisphere America and Eurasia were moving away from each other although the North Atlantic Ocean had not yet fully opened. Further south, Africa was on a northerly collision course with southern Europe and India had began its northerly journey towards collision with Asia.

North America

Europe

South America

Africa

63 - Collin Glen above Belfast provides a good opportunity to examine rocks of Triassic, Jurassic and Cretaceous age. The rocks pictured here occur near the top of the glen and are of Cretaceous age. They comprise green sandstones and mudstones, the green colour coming from the mineral glauconite which is present in the rocks. We know these sandstones and mudstones formed in a shallow sea as glauconite is only found in such an environment.

the Collin Glen in the Lagan Valley (63) and at Portmuck Bay, on Islandmagee, Co. Antrim. The sea then retreated for a while before a warm and shallow sea drowned, not only all of Ireland but also most of the remaining land areas on Earth. It is estimated that the level of this Cretaceous sea was over 200m higher than sea levels today. Only upland areas would have remained above sea level. These land areas took on a new appearance as the first flowering plants appeared at this time and, although mammals were now common the largest of them was no bigger than a domestic cat. Dinosaurs nevertheless remained dominant. The global sea helped create a warm climate across the Earth and both poles remained free of ice. North-west Europe at this time was in subtropical latitudes, approximately 35°N, and the warm, shallow seas provided an ideal environment for tiny, single-celled organisms called coccoliths. As they died, their tiny shells accumulated on the sea floor and over time became compressed into a special variety of limestone called chalk. Under a high powered microscope, chalk is revealed as being packed with the remains of these coccoliths. The white cliffs that tower above the Antrim coast road are made of chalk. The same white rocks can also be seen along the Causeway Coast, along the escarpments to the east of Limavady, Co. Derry and on the hills above west and north Belfast. Although the chalk formed in tranquil seas we know that conditions at that time in the Cretaceous were not always so

64 - Belshaws Quarry Nature Reserve, in the Lagan Valley above Lisburn, provides a good place to see the white chalk. Chalk is the accumulated and compacted remains of billions of microscopic marine organisms called coccoliths.

quiet as geologists have identified many subtle divisions in the chalk. These divisions indicate that, at times, deposition of the lime mud on the sea floor was interrupted. The chalk is one of the most easily accessible rocks to examine in the entire region. Belshaws Quarry (64) and Collin Glen in the Lagan Valley, along the Antrim Coast Road at Glenarm and Garron Point, and at Ballintoy Harbour, White Park Bay and the White Rocks (65) along the Causeway Coast are all ideal.

However, if the Cretaceous sea is supposed to have covered all of Ireland why, with one tiny exception in Co. Kerry, is the chalk only seen in the north-east? Towards the end of Cretaceous times, the sea retreated and erosion quickly removed the soft chalk. But a major geological event was to shake the north-east and help preserve the chalk of this area. This event was again related to the movements of the Earth's tectonic plates. By 65 million years ago South America had pulled away from Africa allowing the creation of the South Atlantic Ocean. Antarctica had also drifted away from these two continents although it remained attached to Australia. India was now on a northerly collision course with Asia while North America and Africa were drifting further apart, opening up the Central Atlantic. While North America pulled away westwards, Africa was heading north towards Europe. We now also know, that at this time, 65 million years ago, these plate movements were resulting in major volcanic activity and as sea levels began to fall climates began to change. Also at this

65 - *The distinctive white cliffs formed by the Cretaceous chalk are characteristic of the Antrim Coast Road, the Causeway Coast and along the western and southern edges of the Antrim Plateau . The White Rocks (pictured here), along the Causeway Coast near Portrush, are a good place to look more closely at the chalk. Although chalk is packed with the fossilised remains of billions of microscopic organisms called coccoliths, some larger fossils can be seen with the unaided eye. These include spear shaped belemnites (a squid-like animal) and Cretaceous sea-urchins. The chalk is also famous as a source of flint and bands of flint can be seen in the cliffs here.*

time, a large comet or small asteroid collided with the Earth. Although the impact site lay in the newly formed Gulf of Mexico, we believe that the consequences of the impact were felt world-wide. Dinosaurs on land and ammonites in the sea are just two groups of animals that became extinct in this new mass extinction of life. This extinction marked not only the end of the Cretaceous Period but also the end of the Mesozoic Era, the so-called Age of Replites. It also marked the dawn of the Cenozoic Era and the Palaeogene Period. In north-east Ireland and western Scotland the dawn of the Palaeogene Period (65 – 23 million years ago) was violent. It also marks the time when that most famous of Irish giants, Fionn Mac Cumhail, allegedly first made his mark on the landscape. The story of these times can be read today in the rocks of the Causeway Coast and in the mountains of Mourne, Cooley and Gullion.

Causeway Coast

The giant awakes

The mass extinction at the end of the Cretaceous Period 65 million years ago heralded the dawn of a new era when mammals became the dominant animals on land. Many strange and exotic mammals evolved during the subsequent Palaeogene Period (65 – 23 million years ago) and many of these mammals seem as strange to us today as the dinosaurs did before them. The continents continued their relentless drift across the Earth's surface (66). Australia broke away from Antarctica and although the latter became stuck over southern polar regions, warm ocean currents ensured that Antarctica remained largely ice free. 60 million years ago, North America once more tried to break away from Europe. This time, however, the resulting rift in the Earth's crust that this movement created lay not down the middle of the North Sea, but further west, in a line along western Scotland and north-east Ireland. As the Earth's crust was stretched and thinned great fractures, or fissures, opened up and huge flows of lava erupted out through them to flood the chalk landscape. Over a period of two

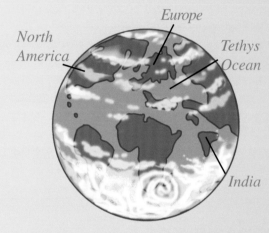

66 - The Palaeogene world of 65 - 23 million years ago. India was moving into collision with Asia and, in the process, creating the Himalayan Mountains. The Tethys Ocean was now much reduced in size and, as the North Atlantic Ocean opened and widened, North America and Europe were forced apart.

million years these volcanic eruptions built up a plateau formed mostly from lava flows of the igneous rock basalt. The remains of this volcanic plateau still cover much of County Antrim and parts of adjacent counties and many features created by volcanic activity can still be seen. However, the most spectacular features associated with this period of volcanism are seen along the Causeway Coast (67).

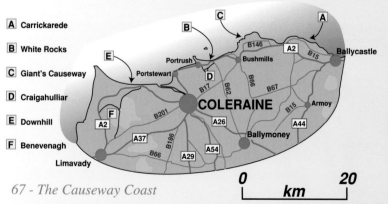

A Carrickarede

B White Rocks

C Giant's Causeway

D Craigahulliar

E Downhill

F Benevenagh

67 - The Causeway Coast

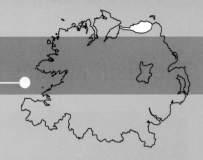

68 - *The rope bridge at Carrickarede is popular with summer visitors. But how many of those visitors crossing the bridge realise they are crossing the mouth of an extinct volcano? In the cliffs below the bridge large blocks of dark basalt can be seen embedded in a sandy coloured material. This material is volcanic ash which was erupted here approximately 60 million years ago!*

Volcanic activity commenced with a series of explosive volcanic eruptions during which large quantities of volcanic ash and debris were erupted. A good example of the volcanic ash erupted at this time can be seen in the cliffs at Carrickarede along the Causeway Coast (68). Here, as you cross the rope bridge, look back at the cliffs on the mainland and note the large blocks of dark rock (basalt) embedded in the sandy coloured rock. This latter rock is the volcanic ash. By looking further east and west along the cliffs here it is apparent that this ash rises vertically through the white chalk. This indicates that this was the actual site of the volcano! Thankfully, the Carrickarede volcano is now long extinct. A further example of this explosive activity is seen east of the car park at the White Rocks near Portrush, Co. Antrim where dark basalt cuts vertically through the chalk. Much further south, Tardree Hill north-east of Antrim town marks the site of a former explosive volcano (69). A forest walk takes you to a disused quarry, now a Nature reserve, where the igneous rock rhyolite can be seen. This rhyolite was erupted as lava during violent eruptions that rocked this area some 60 million years ago. After this explosive phase, lava was erupted quietly through fissures to build up the plateau (70). Lava flows from this period of activity can be seen in the Belfast Hills. Here, notches along the hillsides, represent breaks between successive lava flows. These lavas are also seen along the coastal path at Blackhead, near Carrickfergus, Co. Antrim where small gas-filled cavities were stretched along the direction of flow as the lava moved. Many of these cavities are now filled with minerals such as calcite. After this period of activity ceased, the basalt lava was weathered and eroded. At this time north-east Ireland experienced a wet, sub-tropical climate and

69 - The nature reserve at Tardree Hill north-east of Antrim Town preserves the igneous rock rhyolite in a disused quarry. Unlike the basalt, which erupted quietly through fissures, the rhyolite erupted violently through explosive volcanoes.

weathering of the basalt produced a reddish-brown soil or laterite, rich in iron and alumina. This layer can be identified in many places around the plateau and, at Cargan, Co. Antrim, it was actively mined for iron and aluminium ore. This layer can also be seen around the headlands at the Giant's Causeway and on the path down to the Causeway from the visitors centre (71). Here large rounded blocks of unweathered basalt occur within the laterite forming the so-called "Giant's Eyes". Further down the path further rounded blocks of weathered basalt can be seen in the actual lava flows. This type of weathering is referred to as "spheroidal" or "onion-skin" weathering.

It was along the Causeway Coast that this period of volcanic dormancy was interrupted by a localised series of volcanic eruptions. In several places, lava from these eruptions became dammed in small channels and valleys to form lava-lakes. This lava cooled very slowly allowing a characteristic columnar pattern of cracks, or joints, to develop. The Giant's Causeway is one place where the columns formed as a result of this slow cooling process can be seen (72). They can also be seen at Craigahulliar Quarry, near Coleraine, by arranging access with Coleraine Borough Council (Technical Services Department). Of course

71 - The prominent reddish layer visible in the headlands around the Giant's Causeway is the remains of an iron-rich soil that developed from the weathering of lava in a wet, sub-tropical climate. This soil development happened during a short-lived interruption of the volcanic activity that rocked this area some 60 million years ago.

72 - The Giant's Causeway: Ireland's premier geological attraction. The hexagonal columns of basalt formed as molten lava was allowed to cool very slowly after becoming trapped, or ponded, in a river valley. Hammer shaft is 30cm long for scale but please note that as the Giant's Causeway is a World Heritage Site no geological hammering or sampling is permitted.

there is an alternative explanation for the formation of the basalt columns of the Giant's Causeway, one that involves that most famous of Irish giants, Fionn Mac Cumhail! Indeed, Fionn can challenge geologists for another of the regions most notable landscape features. Not only is Fionn alleged to have created the Causeway in an attempt to reach his Scottish rival Benandonner, he is also supposed to have created Lough Neagh when, in anger, he hurled a piece of Ireland at his rival across the water! Needless to say, however, geologists have a different explanation for that also.

After the localised eruption of these Causeway Basalts, the period of dormancy resumed. Eventually however, widespread volcanic activity returned across all of north-east Ireland as basalt lava once again flooded out of fissures, building up the final layers of the Antrim Plateau. Lava from these eruptions can be seen in the cliffs backing Downhill Strand, Co. Derry or along the shore of Lough Neagh at Shane's Castle, Co. Antrim. This lava also forms the cap to the spectacular cliffs of Benevenagh that shadow the Roe Valley near Limavady, Co. Derry (73). As in Iceland today, fissure eruptions are characterised by chains of small volcanic centres through which the lava erupts. The remains of many of these centres can be seen across north-east Ireland. Probably the most famous of these volcanic plugs is Slemish, near Ballymena (74). Scawt Hill and nearby Ballygalley Head, Co. Antrim, are another two. Carnmoney Hill in Newtownabbey, Co. Antrim is another as are the hills of Sandy Braes and Lyells Hill in south Antrim.

70 - By the close of the Cretaceous Period, 65 million years ago, the Central Atlantic Ocean had already formed as the Americas and Eurasia began to move apart. During the early Palaeogene, this movement continued and, as stresses in the Earth's crust built up, new fractures appeared between Europe and North America. Vast quantities of basaltic lava poured out of these fractures, or fissures, and over a period of only a few million years a large lava plateau was formed. However, this volcanic activity eventually ceased as volcanic activity moved to the north-west. It was here that continental separation eventually succeeded and, as new oceanic crust was created in the intervening gap, the North Atlantic Ocean was formed. This volcanic activity continues today as the Atlantic widens further. Fissure eruptions are common on Iceland (e.g. Krafla, 1984) which sits astride the mid-Atlantic ridge, a largely submarine chain of volcanoes that marks the zone where new oceanic crust is forming.

The much reduced remains of the Palaeogene lava plateau still cover much of north-east Ireland with smaller fragments found on the islands off western Scotland, notably Skye and Mull.

73 - *The spectacular views from the basalt cliffs of Benevenagh, near Limavady, extend north and west towards Magilligan Point and the Inishowen peninsula and south over the Roe Valley towards the Sperrin Mountains. The basalt forming the cliffs here are among the youngest of the lava flows that built up the Antrim plateau during early Palaeogene times some 58 - 60 million years ago. Just as with the cliffs along the Antrim coast, the cliffs here are also underlain by Cretaceous chalk and Jurassic mudstone and evidence of landslides can again be seen.*

Some 58 million years ago volcanic activity in north-east Ireland ceased. The centre of rifting between North America and Europe moved to the west where, eventually, the two plates began to move apart allowing for the formation of the North Atlantic Ocean. This rifting is still happening and is evident by the continuing volcanic activity along the mid-Atlantic ridge, a range of mostly submarine volcanic mountains that run down the centre of the Atlantic Ocean. In several places this ridge reaches above sea level, most notably on Iceland where the same forces that gave rise to the volcanic scenery of Antrim can be seen in action today, creating and shaping the modern landscape of Iceland. However, 60 million years ago not only was there igneous activity at the surface in north-east Ireland, there was significant activity underground as well. To find out how that activity has helped shape our landscape today we move south, to the Mountains of Mourne, the Cooley Mountains and the Ring of Gullion.

74 - *Slemish, near Ballymena, Co. Antrim, is one example of the many volcanic plugs that can be found dotted around the volcanic Antrim Plateau. It was through such plugs that molten magma moved upwards and, in many instances, erupted at the surface as lava.*

Mourne, Gullion & Cooley

Erosion of great volcanoes

The landscape of south Down, south Armagh and north Louth is today dominated by uplands (75). Indeed this small region contains the highest peaks in all of Ireland (north) with Slieve Donard at 852m dominating the skyline above the seaside resort of Newcastle, Co. Down. While Slieve Donard and the rest of the Mourne Mountains dominate the landscape of south Down, the majestic peaks of Slieve Foye and the Cooley Mountains tower over north Louth and form the setting for that most famous of Irish legends, the Táin which tells the story of Cuchulainn's defence of Ulster against the forces of Queen Medbh of Connacht. Nearby the brooding mass of Slieve Gullion south-west of Newry is surrounded by an almost unbroken ring of hills (the Ring of Gullion). Although forming uplands today, the rocks that make up these mountains were mostly formed from molten magma that cooled underground in this area at much the same time as lava was erupting through fissures further north in County Antrim. As North America and Europe tried to pull away from each other 60 million years ago, the Earth's crust stretched, fractured and, as rock at depth was melted, large amounts of magma were generated, much of which was erupted at the surface as lava. This lava gradually built up a basalt plateau, the remains of which today cover much of County Antrim and parts of counties Derry, Tyrone, Armagh and Down. These surface eruptions were however followed by another upwelling of molten magma from deep in the Earth's crust. This magma was different in chemistry to the magma that

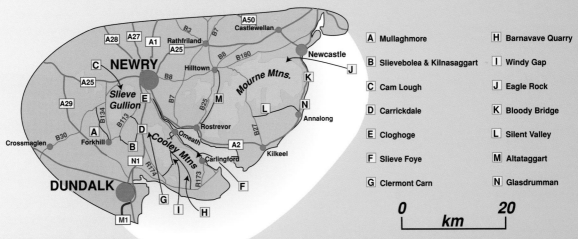

A Mullaghmore		**H** Barnavave Quarry
B Slievebolea & Kilnasaggart		**I** Windy Gap
C Cam Lough		**J** Eagle Rock
D Carrickdale		**K** Bloody Bridge
E Cloghoge		**L** Silent Valley
F Slieve Foye		**M** Altataggart
G Clermont Carn		**N** Glasdrumman

75 - Mourne, Gullion & Cooley

Erosion of great volcanoes

generated the basalt lava and when it broke the surface, explosive eruptions occurred and large volcanoes were built up. Some of this magma remained below the surface where it cooled to form intrusive igneous rocks. Although subsequent erosion has removed much of the evidence of these large volcanoes the eroded roots of two still exist. Slieve Gullion and the encircling Ring of Gullion mark the location of one of the volcanoes while the Cooley Mountains mark the site of the other. The Mourne Mountains, by contrast, mark the site of a third pulse of magma. Here however no surface volcano developed as the magma failed to break the surface and cooled underground.

76 - The Ring of Gullion is an almost unbroken ring of hills that surround the brooding mass of Slieve Gullion in the centre. The ring follows the line of a circular fracture, or fault, in the Earth's crust that resulted from igneous activity in this area approximately 58 million years ago.

The hills of the Ring of Gullion follow a circular geological fracture, or ring fault, around the central mass of Slieve Gullion (76). This ring fault is some 11km across and movement along it, some 58 million years ago may have caused the catastrophic collapse of the crater zone, or caldera, of the central volcano. In some places along the ring fault, magma welled up resulting in explosive eruptions at the surface. Evidence of these eruptions, in the form of explosive vents filled with the igneous rock agglomerate, can be traced from Mullaghbane Mountain, through Forkhill to Slievenabolea above Kilnasaggart. Elsewhere most of the rocks that now define the ring are intrusive igneous rocks such as felsite and granophyre. The contact between the ring-dyke granophyre and the older rock into which it was intruded can be seen in a disused quarry beside an amenity site along the shores of Cam Lough, near Newry. Here the contact can be seen along

77 - Molten magma welled up into the ring fault that formed in this area 58 million years ago. In some places the magma reached the surface, where it erupted, often violently, as lava. Elsewhere, such as here near Camlough, the magma cooled below the surface to form dolerite. The dolerite in this photograph is grey and is in contact (along the dotted red line) with the much older granodiorite which is the lighter coloured rock.

the north face of the quarry (77). Cam Lough itself lies along the line of another, though younger, geological fault and it is erosion by ice along this fault-line that has given the lough its elongate shape (78). The main Dublin – Belfast road crosses the ring dyke in two places. Travelling north from Dundalk the ring dyke intersects the road at Carrickdale, Co. Louth and again at Cloghoge just south of the Newry by-pass. Slieve Gullion itself is the eroded remains of the former volcano but the rocks now exposed on its slopes cooled underground in the roots of this volcano. The Slieve Gullion forest drive will take you past several examples of these intrusive igneous rocks. A small disused quarry, at the most southerly point on the drive, contains examples of an igneous rock that formed by a very unusual process. Here the country rock into which the magma was intruded was itself a much older igneous rock called granodiorite. This granodiorite was progressively altered by incorporation into the magma to form the new igneous rocks, granophyre and granite. The summit car park is opposite a crag of another intrusive igneous

78 - Tranquil Cam Lough, to the west of Newry, is elongate in shape and sits astride a fracture, or fault, in the Earth's crust. This fault is younger than the ring-fault that forms the Ring of Gullion as the ring is offset by a few hundred metres either side of this Camlough Fault.

rock called dolerite. Dolerite has the same chemical composition as basalt but differs from it because, unlike basalt, it failed to reach the surface as lava and cooled more slowly underground giving the rock a coarser-grained appearance. The dolerite here forms a sill which was intruded into the surrounding rock as a horizontal layer (like the filling of a sandwich!). The rock into which it was intruded is a variety of granite which, to geologists, is very exciting as dolerite and granite are at opposite ends of the chemical spectrum as far as igneous rocks are concerned. As such it is very unusual to find the two rocks developed in the same place and at the same time.

The Cooley Mountains similarly represent the ancient and eroded roots of a large volcano which was also active about 60 million years ago. Although the craggy summit of Slieve Foye (Carlingford Mountain) today stands at 589m above sea level, 60 million years ago both it and Slieve Gullion formed part of enormous volcanoes that would have stood much higher (79). Three main rock types are now found in the Cooley Mountains, gabbro, dolerite and granophyre. All are intrusive igneous rocks that formed by the solidification of molten magma deep below the volcanoes surface. The gabbro and dolerite were intruded first and the impressive arc of mountains formed by Slieve Foye, Eagles Rock and Foxes Rock contains over 360m of gabbro, intruded as layers (80. The gabbro and dolerite was followed by the

Erosion of great volcanoes

79 - Slieve Foye, or Carlingford Mountain, is formed from the igneous rocks gabbro and dolerite. They were formed below a large volcano that existed here in early Palaeogene times.

injection of granophyre. The main area of granophyre underlies the relatively low ground in the centre of the Cooley Mountains although Clermont Carn, at 510m, is also made of granophyre. The rounded shape of the granophyre hills of west Cooley is in marked contrast to the jagged topography of the gabbro highlands of east Cooley.

Just as at Slieve Gullion, there is evidence in Cooley of the mixing of the two magmas that gave rise to the gabbro and granophyre. At Barnavave Quarry, southwest of Carlingford, both gabbro and granophyre are mixed together. Here the earlier gabbro was injected into a limestone which has been metamorphosed by the heat of the magma. New and rare minerals formed in the limestone as a result of this change. Further north, at the Windy Gap, a geological fault separates the gabbro from the granphyre. The darker coloured gabbro is seen north of the road while the paler granophyre is seen to the south. The fault created a weakness in the rock here (note how the granophyre is badly fractured) which erosion took advantage of to widen, creating the gap we see today. An amenity site just north of Carlingford village, on the road to Omeath, lies beneath a prominent rocky outcrop. The rock here comprises beds of mudstone and sandstone, which

80 - Eagles Rock on the northern flank of Carlingford Mountain is composed of layers of the igneous rock gabbro. These layers reach over 360m in total thickness in this part of Cooley.

69

81 - Thin sheets of molten magma were intruded into the rocks around the margins of the Cooley volcano in Palaeogene times. This magma cooled to form dolerite and in this photograph the darker coloured dolerite of the cone-sheet can be seen intruded into the lighter coloured granophyre. This example is from the Windy Gap. Hammer shaft is 30cm long for scale.

formed as horizontal layers on the floor of the ancient Iapetus Ocean over 450 million years ago. The continental collisions that led to the closure of this ocean forced these layers into the vertical position we see today. During the early Palaeogene, some 60 million years ago, these rocks were injected by layers or sheets of molten magma that solidified to dolerite. These thin sheets of dolerite, termed cone sheets, are typically formed around the margins of large volcanoes. Although this is the best place to see them in Cooley, they can also be seen in the Windy Gap (81).

On the northern side of beautiful Carlingford Lough are the Mountains of Mourne (82). They too are formed from intrusive igneous rocks, in this case granites which are some 56 million years old. However they differ from those in Cooley and the Ring of Gullion in that they do not contain any evidence that the magma here ever reached the surface and erupted as lava from a volcano. We know this because the roof of the magma chamber, formed by the older sediments into which the magma was intruded, still exists in places. Nevertheless the Mourne granites were intruded at a high level within the Earth's crust unlike the older granites in Donegal which formed at greater depths. The Mourne granites were intruded by successive injections of molten magma at two centres. The

82 - The Mountains of Mourne near Attical, Co. Down.

Erosion of great volcanoes

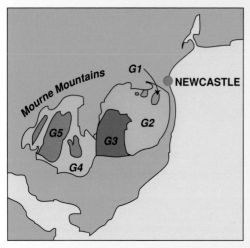

83 - A map showing the distribution of the Mourne granites

eastern centre has three distinctive granites (i.e. three intrusions of magma) while the western centre has two (83). In each case the intrusions are arranged within one another and they occurred at sufficiently long intervals to allow each granite mass to cool and solidify before the intrusion of the next pulse of magma. The five granite intrusions that together make up the Mourne Mountains are imaginatively called G1, G2, G3, G4 and G5!

In the eastern Mournes, the granites have been sufficiently eroded to show parts of the roof and walls of the intrusions. The crags at the base of the cliff at Eagle Rock, high above Donard Park in Newcastle, show a pale coloured granite (G2) cooled against a roof formed by an older, dark granite (G1). The contact between the granites and the much older sedimentary rocks into which they were all intruded can be seen along the Glen River, again above Donard Park, and also along the Bloody Bridge River, south of Newcastle. In both cases the contacts (G2) are some 90

84 - Granites are often characterised by their patterns of joints and fractures. The photograph on the left, taken at the Castles of Commedagh, shows how weathering has emphasised the joint pattern. The photograph on the right, taken at the Hare's Gap shows the more usual appearance of granite jointing.

minutes walk from the carparks at Donard Park and Bloody Bridge. By continuing further up the path beside the Bloody Bridge River the track (called the Brandy Pad) eventually passes below the southern sides of the summits of Slieve Donard and Slieve Commedagh, the two highest peaks in the Mournes. The summits of both mountains are formed from the G1 granite seen at Eagles Rock. Again along the Brandy Pad, and roughly midway between the two peaks are the Castles of Commedagh (84). These are spectacularly weathered pillars of G2 granite. The granite here however is very badly rotted and no climbing should be attempted. The Silent Valley, in the central Mournes, lies in the heart of the G3 granite. It can be seen in several disused quarries along many of the walking trails here. At a quarry above the eastern side of the Ben Crom Reservoir, a dolerite dyke can be seen intruding into the G3 granite. The lower mountains of the western Mournes are composed of the G4 and G5 granites. From the car park at Leitrim Lodge, on the more eastern of the two roads north from Rostrevor to Hilltown, a walk south along the western slopes of Altataggart Mountain brings you past many examples of the G5 granite. A short walk from the same car park north-east to the summit of Rocky Mountain will take you to exposures of a white-coloured granite and a pink-coloured granite. The white granite is the G5 granite while the distinctive pinkish one is the G4 granite. As in parts of the Cooley Mountains, the oldest Mourne granites were intruded into much older sandstones and mudstones. Again these were metamorphosed in a thin zone adjacent to the granites by the heat of the magma. Also, as at Cooley, cone-sheets of dolerite were intruded around the granites. These can easily be seen along the Mourne Coastal Path at Glasdrumman Port and south from Annalong where the dark dolerite is in marked contrast to the pale coloured sedimentary rocks (85).

As well as forming the cone-sheets around the Cooley and Mourne Mountains, dolerite was injected into rocks all over northern Ireland as the period of volcanic activity in the early Palaeogene drew to a close. This dolerite formed sills and dykes which can be seen today from the shores of Killala Bay, Co. Sligo, in the west to Carrickfergus, Co. Antrim, in the east where it forms the rock upon which the Normans built their castle (86). After the intrusion of the dolerite, the

85 - As on the Cooley peninsula, cone-sheets were formed around the margins of the Mourne granite complex. At Glasdrumman Port along the Mourne Coastal Path, these cone sheets can be seen as the dark rock (dolerite) intruded into older, paler coloured rock (sandstones and greywackes of Silurian age).

Erosion of great volcanoes

Irish landscape became a much quieter place. However, nature had not yet finished moulding our landscape and the last two pieces of the jigsaw still remained to be put in place.

86 - Carrickfergus Castle, Co. Antrim, was built upon a dolerite dyke of Palaeogene age. As the molten magma, which later cooled to form the dolerite, came into contact with the Jurassic mudstones of the area, it baked and altered them for a short distance on either side. Dykes of this age are common right across northern Ireland.

Lough Neagh

Lakes ancient and new

Throughout the Palaeogene Period (65 – 23 million years ago) Ireland continued to drift north (66). The climate was warm and wet and gradually Ireland, together with the rest of Europe, took on an increasingly familiar shape. Mammals, which had taken over from dinosaurs as the main group of land animals, began to colonise the sea as the first whales evolved. By 25 million years ago grasses had spread worldwide giving the landscape a new appearance. While the North Atlantic Ocean continued to widen to the west, South America had finally separated from Antarctica. Still stuck over southern polar regions but now totally surrounded by the sea, Antarctica became engulfed by a thick ice sheet. As the ice sheet grew, global sea levels fell and more dry land appeared. India began to make contact with Asia, a collision which resulted in the formation of the Himalayas and which is continuing to this day. Animals such as horse, rhinoceras, deer, cattle and pig appeared. Around this time the first apes were also appearing.

In north-east Ireland the young basalt lava flows had cooled and the plateau these flows had built up was being eroded. Older fractures, or faults, that existed under the plateau formed weaknesses in the Earth's crust that began to give way under the weight of the basalt. By 25 million years ago large depressions, or basins, developed which began to fill with water as rivers emptied into them. The erosion of the basalt and older rocks to the south and west allowed these rivers to carry large quantities of fine sediment into these lakes which collected on the lake bed as clay. These lake clays today form the youngest rocks in Ireland and they underlie much of the area beneath Ballymoney, Co. Antrim and much of the area below the direct descendent of one of those Palaeogene lakes, the present day Lough Neagh (87). The presence of clay around the shores of southern Lough Neagh have been known for centuries but it was only in the past few decades that drilling has indicated their full extent. Beneath Washing Bay in the south-west corner of the lough, the clays are over 340m thick. They extend for over 300km^2 under southern Lough Neagh and for another 200km^2 under parts of the adjacent counties.

87 - Lough Neagh; the largest lake in Ireland and Britain.

Lakes ancient and new

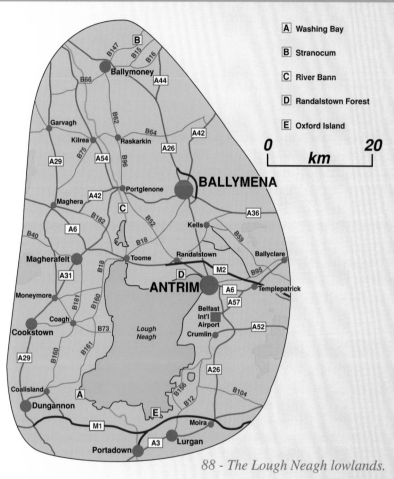

A Washing Bay
B Stranocum
C River Bann
D Randalstown Forest
E Oxford Island

88 - The Lough Neagh lowlands.

The same clay also occurs in parts of north Derry and north Antrim, roughly from Garvagh, through Ballymoney to Stranocum, (88). Although the sediments that were deposited in these late Palaeogene lakes was mostly clay some sandstone and conglomerate was also deposited.

Lignite, or brown coal, was also formed at this time and large deposits of this resource now occur near Crumlin, Co. Antrim and, again further north, under Ballymoney. The lignite was formed in swampy environments around the shores of these ancient lakes (89). It is believed that, as vegetation decayed in this environment, floating or raised peat swamps formed. These swamps would have been flooded by the lake waters that drowned and preserved the peat which, as it was buried, was compressed into lignite. Study of the lignite has revealed the presence of tiny fossils preserved within it. Some of these fossils are spores that indicate trees such as palms, cypress, conifers and ferns flourished here at that time. This type of vegetation suggests that the climate around the Lough Neagh area 25 million years ago was warm and frost-free. Unfortunately, the lignite

and the clay are mostly obscured by a thick layer of material left behind by melting ice sheets at the end of the last Ice Age and little is seen at the surface. However, occasionally some pieces of petrified wood, associated with the lignite, can be found along the lough shore. The shape of Lough Neagh has changed many times since the Palaeogene lakes vanished. As the last Ice Age began to retreat some 13,000 years ago ice blocked the path of the River Bann as it drained north, forcing the Bann to find an outlet to the sea further south. The lough itself was considerably larger at that time and it is believed that the Bann flowed south to Carlingford Lough, approximately along the line of the present day Newry Canal. Since then the levels of Lough Neagh have dropped, firstly as a natural process as the Bann drained north to the sea near Coleraine and then subsequently, and very recently, as a result of the actions of Man. In an attempt to control winter flood levels of the lough, Man has endeavoured to lower the lough level. This artificial lowering of the lough has only occurred in the last few decades and the former shorelines of the lough can be seen in several places around the lough shore. One such place is at Randalstown Forest on the northern shore and another is at Oxford Island (no longer an island!) on the southern shore (90).

90 - Lough Neagh at Oxford Island. The terraces, marked by the tree line, were formed during periods of time when the water levels in the lough were higher than those today.

Although the Lough Neagh clays and lignites constitute the youngest rocks in Ireland our Story Through Time does not end here. Following the end of the Palaeogene Period 23 million years ago, the Neogene Period commenced. It lasted from 23 to only 1.6 million years ago. This was a period of erosion across Ireland (north) and no rocks from this time exist today. We believe that sea levels were slightly higher than they are today but by 2 million years ago the shape of Ireland and Europe looked very similar to those of today. At the start of Neogene times, India had collided with Asia and as Africa drifted north it began to collide with southern Europe. Italy, which at that time formed part of Africa, was driven into central Europe, the resulting collision creating the Alps. This collision also created a large depression between Europe and Africa that would subsequently be flooded by the Atlantic to create the Mediterranean Sea. Hominids, of which we are a species, appeared 15 million years ago and by 3 million years ago, some groups of hominids were developing human-like characteristics. Animals such as the sabre-toothed tiger and close relatives of the elephant, such as the *Mastodon,* were also common at this time. However, global climates then started to cool. The southern ice cap expanded and in the northern hemisphere the northern polar cap also began to grow. By 1,600,000 years ago great ice sheets had expanded to cover vast areas of the northern continents as the Earth became locked in the grip of ice. The Great Ice Age had begun.

Lakes ancient and new

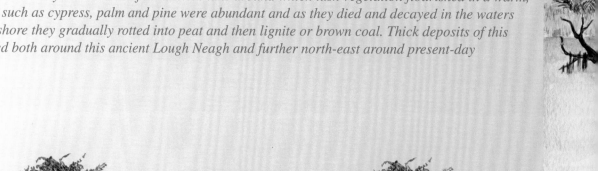

89 - Various legends are told about the origin of Lough Neagh. First there is the story of the overflowing well. According to this story an old woman, who had custody of an enchanted well, forgot to close the gate of the enclosure surrounding the well which subsequently overflowed to create the lough we see today. Then there is the story of the underground city which had a magical spring. As the inhabitants of the city became greedy and warlike the spring took its revenge on them by drowning the city and everyone in it. Finally there is the story of Fionn Mac Cumhail who, not content with creating the Giant's Causeway, hurled a huge sod of land towards his Scottish rival. His aim was somewhat amiss and the sod of land fell into the Irish Sea where it formed the Isle of Man. The hole left behind eventually filled with water to create Lough Neagh.

Geologists tell a fourth story. This is one of an ancient lake around which lush vegetation flourished in a warm, wet climate. Trees such as cypress, palm and pine were abundant and as they died and decayed in the waters around the lough shore they gradually rotted into peat and then lignite or brown coal. Thick deposits of this lignite accumulated both around this ancient Lough Neagh and further north-east around present-day Ballymoney.

The Drumlin Belt

The ice advances

The Quaternary Period (1.6 million years ago to the present) marks the most recent of the periods of geological time. Indeed we are currently living in the Quaternary. The dawn of the Quaternary Period saw the Earth gripped in the cold of the Ice Age (91). Over the last 1,600,000 years the ice has advanced and retreated many times with each episode of ice advance (called a glaciation) lasting approximately 100,000 years. Between these glaciations the climate warms and each period of climatic warmth (called an interglacial) has typically lasted around 10,000 to 60,000 years. At the peak of the last glaciation, about 18,000 years ago the Antarctic ice sheet would have been double its present size and in the northern hemisphere ice covered much of Canada and northern Europe, including Ireland and Britain. In parts of Europe the ice was over 3,000m thick! Many animals such as the woolly mammoth and the woolly rhinoceras adapted to the cold conditions on the fringes of the great ice sheets (92). In the warmer areas of the world, this was also the time when human evolution finally took off and by 30,000 years ago modern Man had appeared. The last glaciation finally retreated into high polar regions only 13,000 years ago and today we live in an interglacial period. In all likelihood the ice will once again advance in the future plunging the world into another glaciation.

91 - For the last 1.6 million years the polar ice caps have periodically expanded burying large parts of the northern hemisphere in thick ice sheets. During these times global sea levels dropped creating land bridges such as those that developed between Ireland and Scotland, England and France and Siberia and Alaska.

In Europe, evidence for six major glaciations has been uncovered. In Ireland (north) however only the most recent glaciation has left substantial evidence of its existence. This is because each new advance of the ice effectively removes the evidence of the previous glaciation. Four main stages in the development of this last glaciation have been recognised. Firstly, there is evidence of ice moving east or north from a centre over the Donegal Highlands. This ice was then joined by ice moving south and west across the region from Scotland. Thirdly these ice sheets were joined by ice moving east and north from the Irish midlands. At this stage a great dome of ice covered most of Ireland, with the greatest thickness of ice probably over the Lough Neagh or Sperrin Mountains area. After this advance, the climate warmed and the ice began to melt. However, approximately 13,000 years ago ice from Scotland briefly readvanced into north-east Ireland before the warmer conditions resumed. The effects of this last great

93 - *U-shaped valleys, carved by advancing glaciers during the last Ice Age are found across all the upland areas of northern Ireland. The example to the left is Glenariff in Co. Antrim while the example below is Glengesh, in south-west Donegal. The prefix "glen", so common across both Ireland and Scotland, comes from the Gaelic word "gleann" meaning valley.*

glaciation can be seen all across Ireland (north). The broad U-shaped valleys of Glenariff (Co. Antrim), Glenfarne (Co. Leitrim), and Glenveagh (Co. Donegal) were all carved by glaciers (93). As the ice melted large quantities of clay and till which it carried were deposited over the landscape blanketing most of it in a thick layer. However while the influence of the Ice Age can be seen right across the region, its affects are perhaps most noticeable in two areas. The Sperrin Mountains marks the place where a section of the last ice sheet melted away and the Drumlin Belt, which stretches from Co. Cavan, through Monaghan and Armagh to Co. Down, is typified by the numerous small, elongate hills of clay which the ice sheet moulded as it advanced (94).

Throughout the Drumlin Belt place names relate closely to features in the landscape. Cavan, or An Cabhán, means "the hollow" and refers to the fact that the town is built in a hollow between several small, rounded hills. Monaghan, or Muineachán, means place of little hills. Armagh, or Ard Macha, means the heights of Macha (a mythical Irish princess) and it was these heights, or hills, that St. Patrick chose as the centre of his Christian mission to Ireland. Dromore (Co. Down), or Droim Mhór, means the large hill. These small rounded hills are so numerous that the Celts even had a specific name for them, they called them "dromnín" and it is from this that we derive the English word "drumlin" which is used world-wide for these little, rounded hills that were moulded by the ice. Although most of the

92 - *The Greater Belfast area as it might have looked only few tens of thousand of years ago. For several hundred years either side of a major glaciation, large areas on the edge of the ice sheet would have experienced tundra-like conditions. The ground would have been permanently frozen at depth and each summer only the top few metres would have thawed out. Animals such as the woolly mammoth (1), the musk-oxen (2) and the wolf (3) would have lived in the tundra, competing for the limited food resources that were available. Man too would have existed in this environment although there is no evidence of his existence in Ireland until 9000 years ago, well after the retreat of the last ice sheets.*

As the ice retreated, global sea levels at first rose and newly-established land-bridges across the northern hemisphere were severed. One such bridge lay between Inishowen in Co. Donegal and the Scottish islands of Islay and Jura. This bridge was flooded before the English - French bridge was broken and this limited the diversity of plants and animals that were able to colonise the new ice-free Ireland from mainland Europe. By contrast, Britain, which remained connected to the mainland for a longer period, has a greater diversity of plants and animals. It was at this time that the land bridges linking the Florida peninsula to the Flordia Keys and that linking Alaska and Siberia were also broken. Eventually, the land began to rebound upwards now that is was free of the weight of the ice. Beaches that were formed during the periods of higher sea level were raised and former sea-stacks and sea-caves were lifted above the high water mark.

2

drumlins are made totally of glacial boulder clay, some do have solid rock at their core and a few are made from sand and gravel. The drumlins are so numerous across Counties Cavan, Monaghan, Armagh and Down that they give rise to landscape that looks like a "basket of eggs" when seen from a height. This landscape is obvious when seen from Loughanlea, near Bailieborough, Co. Cavan, or from Saul Hill just east of Downpatrick, Co. Down. The drumlins vary is size and height but they typically stand 10 to 30m high and the intervening low ground is characterised by its poor drainage due to the glacial clay. Small lakes often form in these hollows, such as Corbet Lough, near Banbridge, Co. Down. Larger lakes also formed due to the poor drainage and as the waters of these lakes rose they developed convoluted shapes, filling the low ground between adjacent drumlins. Lough Oughter and Lough Gowna in Co. Cavan are both typical of these irregularly shaped lakes. Killykeen Forest Park on the shores of Lough Oughter

A	Loughanlea	E	Mahee Island
B	Saul Hill	F	Lough Muckno
C	Corbet Lough	G	Bellamont & Darty Forest
D	Killykeegan	H	Dundonald Gap

94 - The Drumlin Belt

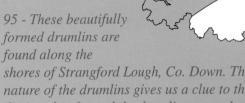

95 - These beautifully formed drumlins are found along the shores of Strangford Lough, Co. Down. The elongate nature of the drumlins gives us a clue to the direction the ice, that formed the drumlins, moved as it advanced over the Pleistocene countryside.

was developed on the tops of drumlins that remain above the level of the lough. The Drumlin Belt also extends into south Co. Fermanagh where the irregular shape of Upper Lough Erne has the same explanation. Here some of the drumlins form island steeping-stones across the lake. Trasna Island straddles the breadth of the lough and carries the main Lisnaskea – Derrylin road. In Co. Down, as the waters of Strangford Lough rose at the end of the last glaciation many of the drumlins here too became isolated as small islands. Some, such as Reagh Island and Mahee Island are attached to the mainland only by narrow causeways. These drowned drumlin islands are known locally as "pladdies" (95).

The elongate nature of the drumlins also gives us clues as to the direction in which the ice advanced. It was the advance of the ice that moulded the clay into drumlins and the long axis of each drumlin is consequently aligned approximately parallel to the direction of ice flow. Detailed investigations of the direction of the long axes of the drumlins reveal that most are roughly aligned north to south or north-east to south-west. This would suggest that the drumlins were formed either as ice from the Midlands moved north or as ice from the Lough Neagh – Sperrins area moved south. In all likelihood, the drumlins probably owe their origin to a combination of both. Those in north-east Down also incorporate an element of the Scottish ice which advanced over this area from the north-east. As the ice sheets of the last glaciation advanced, not only did they mould the drumlins they also scoured the landscape in places. Long, narrow hollows were gouged out which later filled with water to form lakes. Examples of these are seen in Co. Monaghan were Lough Muckno and the numerous lakes in the Bellamont and Dartry Forest are elongate in shape (96).

After the peak of glaciation only 18,000 years ago the ice gradually retreated except for a brief period 13,000 years ago when ice from Scotland briefly impinged along the east Antrim coast and, in north Antrim, advanced inland as far

The ice advances

96 - *The small, rounded hills that border Lough Muckno in Co. Monaghan are drumlins; hills of clay that were moulded by advancing ice during the last Ice Age. These drumlins are part of a swarm of such hills that stretch from the Ards peninsula of Co. Down south-westwards to Co. Longford.*

as Armoy. Here a prominent ridge of glacial debris called moraine marks the furthest limit of this ice. At that time the Scottish ice blocked the normal drainage of many rivers. As already mentioned, the Bann was no longer able to reach the sea near Portstewart. Similarly, the River Lagan was no longer able to drain into Belfast Lough because the ice sheet blocked its way. As a consequence of this, a large lake built up in front of the ice, formed by a combination of water from the Lagan and water from the melting ice. Lough Lagan, as this glacial lake is known, covered much of the present day Lagan Valley and, as its level rose, water began to drain from it into Strangford Lough via the Dundonald Gap. The present day road from Belfast to Newtownards still follows the line of this glacial river, or channel. Water from Lough Lagan also drained into the enlarged Lough Neagh via a channel near Aghalee, Co. Antrim. The present day Broadwater and Friars Glen are the remains of this channel. However the melting ice created many additional landforms and because, geologically, it happened very recently, erosion has not had time to remove or greatly modify them. Perhaps the best place to see these landforms are in the Sperrin Mountains and it is there that we now go for the penultimate chapter in the development of our "Landscapes From Stone".

The Sperrins and The Foyle

The ice melts

We have already seen that during the height of the last glaciation, the ice sheet that covered much of Ireland was probably thickest over central Ulster. Buried deep beneath this ice, the high peaks of the Sperrin Mountains were gradually worn down into the broad, rounded summits we see today (97). As the ice began to melt and retreat northwards, a section of the ice sheet became isolated over the Sperrins and as it gradually wasted away it created a whole series of landforms that today fill the beautiful valleys of Glenelly and Owenkillew in the heart of this region (98). As the ice began to melt rivers not only drained away from the ice margins, but also flowed beneath and within the ice sheet. These glacial rivers carried much sand and gravel that the ice had picked up during its advance across the landscape and these rivers deposited this sediment in ridges parallel to their direction of flow. Many of these ridges are winding in nature and can be up to 30m or more in height. As with the drumlins, these winding ridges are so numerous that the Celts had a special name for them also, they called them "eiscir". This word

97 - *The broad summits of the Sperrin Mountains, seen here from the Glenelly Valley were rounded by ice during the last Ice Age. Their undulating nature belies the fact that these are some of the highest mountains in Ireland (north).*

too has passed into world-wide usage and today the word esker is used to describe these winding ridges of sand and gravel wherever they occur. Examples of eskers can be seen at Eskermore (An Eiscir Mhór – the big esker) near Beragh, Co. Tyrone and at Muntober, west of Cookstown, Co. Tyrone. Indeed eskers and other ridges of glacial sand and gravel can be seen all along the main Cookstown – Omagh road and in several places these deposits are actively quarried as they form a very good resource for the construction industry. This material is also quarried at the southern end of Lough Fea north of Cookstown and high up on the northern slopes of Slieve Gallion. This gives some idea of the former levels of these glacial meltwater streams and rivers. The higher reaches of both the Owenkillew and the Glenelly valleys have many esker-like ridges and, further north in Banagher Forest, part of a similar ridge has been cut away to make room for an amenity site (99). This cross section of an esker offers a good opportunity to see the material that makes up these ridges.

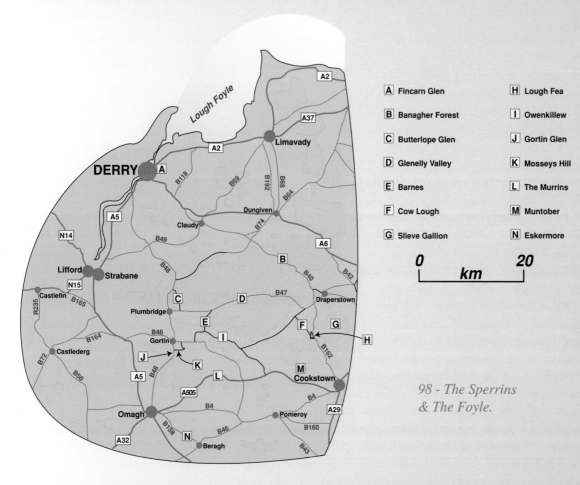

A	Fincarn Glen	**H**	Lough Fea
B	Banagher Forest	**I**	Owenkillew
C	Butterlope Glen	**J**	Gortin Glen
D	Glenelly Valley	**K**	Mosseys Hill
E	Barnes	**L**	The Murrins
F	Cow Lough	**M**	Muntober
G	Slieve Gallion	**N**	Eskermore

0   km   20

98 - The Sperrins & The Foyle.

As with Lough Neagh and the Lagan Valley, the melting of the ice over the Sperrins often blocked the drainage of the rivers and here too large glacial lakes developed. As these lakes drained to the north, further channels were cut just as they were further east in the Lagan Valley. Gortin Glen, Barnes and Butterlope Glen (north of Plumbridge, Co. Tyrone) were all cut by the meltwaters as they drained away north. The full extent of the glacial lakes in this area is unclear but Mosseys Hill, above Gortin, Co. Tyrone is composed of very finely layered silt that was deposited as the meltwater built a delta into glacial Lough Owenkillew. On top of this former delta, large blocks of ice became stranded. Over time, they eventually melted leaving behind large hollows which later filled with water to form lakes. These features are known as "kettle lakes" and the Gortin lakes are very good examples. The numerous small lakes around The Murrins (along the main Omagh – Cookstown road) are further examples as are small lakes such as Mill Lough, Cow Lough and Lough Patrick to the north of Lough Fea, near

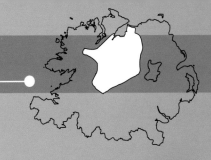

99 - Eskers, winding ridges of sand and gravel formed beneath and within melting ice, are common across the Sperrins and Foyle region. The example top left comes from near Muntober close to the main Omagh - Cookstown road, while the example top right comes from Banagher Forest.

Cookstown (100). As the glacial waters drained away north, they flowed into the River Foyle. Again, the readvance of the Scottish ice briefly blocked the mouth of Lough Foyle which flooded the adjacent lowlands of north Derry. Here too deep overflow channels were cut, such as Fincarn Glen to the east of Derry City

The large amounts of clay, sand and gravel left behind at the end of the Ice Age have largely hidden the rock core of the Sperrins and Foyle area. However, in several places the ancient rocks that make up the mountains do come to the surface. The meltwaters that cut the glens at Gortin, Barnes and Butterlope have also revealed these ancient rocks (101). These rocks are sandstones, limestones and mudstones that have been metamorphosed into schists and pelites. They date from Precambrian times and belong to the Dalradian Supergroup of rocks. Just like the Dalradian rocks in Co. Donegal, they originally formed on the floor of a shallow sea before the creation of the Iapetus Ocean. At Butterlope Glen, the glacial meltwaters have revealed greenish coloured schists at the head of the glen, with examples of quartzite high up in crags on the east side of the glen approximately half way down. Further down the glen, in a disused quarry, are examples of the limestone. Here then, in the heart of the Sperrin Mountains, the Ice Age, that most recent of geological events to have shaped our landscape, has also revealed some of the oldest geological elements that help make up that landscape. In a way, Butterlope Glen together with Barnes and Gortin Gap close the geological circle of our "Story Through Time" from the ancient Dalradian Sea to the last glaciation which ended only a

100 - As the ice-sheets melted, large blocks of ice became stranded in a sea of glacial gravel, sand and silt. Eventually these "icebergs" melted leaving behind a large hollow which later filled with water to form a small lake. These kettle lakes are common across the Sperrins. The example to the left is from the Gortin Lakes, near Omagh, while those below are from the Murrins, between Omagh and Cookstown. Also note the small ridge, or esker, on the left hand side of this photograph.

geological second ago. It is also interesting to ponder that within the Dalradian rocks of south Donegal lies a conglomerate left behind by an ancient Ice Age. Here in the Sperrins a modern Ice Age has revealed the same Dalradian rocks. Elsewhere in the Sperrins however, the blanket of glacial debris has, for many years hidden another secret. Deep within the Dalradian rocks of this area are thin veins of that most treasured of metals – gold!

The gold too is ancient compared to the glacial debris. It formed from hot fluids that circulated within the Dalradian sediments as they were metamorphosed during the collisions that led to the formation of the Caledonian Mountains. Who knows what other secrets these rocks hold. Similarly we cannot predict, as we continue to unlock these secrets using ever more sophisticated techniques, how they will change our interpretation of the rocks and the landscape and how that might, in turn, change the details of our "Story through Time".

101 - Barnes Gap, seen here from the Glenelly Valley, was cut by meltwater from the shrinking ice sheets at the close of the last Ice Age.

The Story Continues...

And finally...

The development of the landscapes of Ireland (north) did not stop with the retreat of the last ice 12,000 years ago (102). Initially global sea levels were low as so much water was locked up in the ice. Land bridges linked continents over which animals, and Man, were able to migrate. Alaska was linked to Siberia by one land bridge and in Europe, Britain was linked to the near continent by a land bridge across the Straits of Dover. Ireland was, in turn, linked to Britain by a narrow land bridge from Malin Head, Co. Donegal to the Hebridean islands of Islay and Jura. However sea levels quickly rose as the ice melted and, as these land bridges disappeared, many low-lying coastal areas were flooded. One such area was Belfast where the Belfast Lough estuary extended as far as High Street. The mud deposited on the floor of this estuary, known locally as sleech, has created many difficulties for builders in central

103 - One of Belfast City's most notable landmarks is the Albert Memorial Clock Tower on High Street. Over the years the tower has developed a noticeable lean caused by the soft material, or sleech, upon which it was built. This sleech was deposited on the floor of Belfast Lough when the estuary extended this far inland as a result of higher sea levels following the melting of the ice.

Belfast. Its unstable nature is also the reason why the famous landmark of the Albert Clock leans so markedly to the side (103). Eventually however, as the climate continued to warm, the land surface started to rise after the weight of the ice was removed and the coastline assumed its present shape. The former shoreline was then left higher and these "raised beaches" can be seen in many places, for example on Islandmagee, Co. Antrim. At Cushendun, Co. Antrim, former sea stacks and sea caves are now above the high water mark and along the North Antrim Coastal Path west of Ballintoy Harbour former sea stacks again are now raised above the high water mark (104).

Although the ice has retreated, at least for the present, the continents are still drifting over the surface of the Earth. This movement will continue to affect Ireland and will continue to shape our landscape. New rocks will form as older ones are eroded. Continents will continue to collide creating new mountain chains just as new oceans will continue to appear. But can we predict what might happen? The short answer is no, but, we can make a good, informed guess of what might happen over the next 50 million years (105). Europe, and

And finally...

102- As the glaciers and ice sheets retreated at the end of the last Ice Age many lakes developed, formed not only from glacial meltwaters but also as a result of river courses becoming dammed by glacial debris or obstructed by the melting ice. One such lake, reconstructed here, was glacial Lake Lagan which covered much of the present day Belfast Lough and parts of Belfast city centre.

After all the ice had melted, global sea levels were higher than those of today and Belfast Lough would have extended as far as High Street in Belfast city centre. Land bridges between Ireland and Scotland were severed as Ireland became an island. After the land bridge between England and France was broken, Britain too became isolated from the rest of Europe. In places however, the land did eventually start to rise again. The immediate post-glacial beaches were raised as the present day coastline took shape. Today, only north-west Scotland and most of Scandinavia continue to rise, the level of the land there still adjusting after the melting of the great Pleistocene ice sheets.

104 - Just west of Ballintoy, Co. Antrim, former sea-stacks, which formed when sea levels were higher following the melting of the ice sheets, are now above the high water mark. This former beach was raised as the land rebounded upwards after the weight of the ice was removed.

Ireland, will continue to drift northwards into polar latitudes. At the same time it will turn clockwise possibly bringing Ireland and Britain into a similar position to present day southern Greenland. Africa too will move northwards but its shape will be somewhat different to that of today. The Great East African Rift valley that carves its way from the Red Sea through east Africa to Mozambique marks the site of a new spreading zone where the African continent is literally splitting in two. As these two fragments drift apart, the Red Sea will widen and a new ocean will form here. The spreading zone will also extend north through the Dead Sea and along the eastern Mediterranean and then north east through central Asia and into Siberia which will then split from Europe. Australia will continue to move north and, in 50 million years time, it should straddle the equator. The Americas will move north westwards as the Pacific Ocean contracts in size. Whether North America and South America remain connected is unlikely. Finally, Antarctica will probably remain stuck fast over the southern polar regions. Whether these movements will mean higher or lower sea levels or indeed the flooding of the Irish landmass no-one knows. Whether volcanism may return again remains unknown. Whether another asteroid or comet might impact the Earth helping to create another major evolutionary break in the development of life, while quite likely, again remains unknown.

105 - Earth as it might look some 50 million years into the future. By then a new ocean will have formed along the line of the present day rift valley of East Africa and the Red Sea. This ocean will extend into the present day Mediterranean basin and into central Asia, separating much of Siberia from Europe. By then, Ireland may have drifted into sub-Arctic latitudes.

Beyond 50 million years not even informed speculation can be used to guess what might happen. The story however will continue, although the pace of change will begin to slow. Eventually, the radioactive heat from the core of the Earth that has driven the movements of the Earth's plates will begin to fade. Plate movement will slow and, at some stage in the distant geological future, it will stop. This will have dire consequences for the planet. The atmosphere will gradually be lost to space and the oceans will disappear. Earth will be geologically dead. We also know that some 5,000,000,000 years in the future the Sun itself will die. As part of that process it will cool and swell in size engulfing the innermost planets of Mercury and Venus (106). Whether anybody, or anything, on Earth will be around to witness these colossal events is very unlikely. By that time our "Story through Time" and the development of our "Landscapes From Stone" will surely have ended.

106 - The Earth is but one of nine planets that orbit the star we know as the Sun. It is the Sun that gives us the light and heat that allows life on Earth to flourish, without it Earth would be as lifeless as the Moon. The interaction of plate tectonic activity on the Earth with the evolution of life has allowed the formation of an atmosphere that is unique in our Solar System. This atmosphere protects us from harmful solar radiation and helps keep the Earth's surface at a temperature comfortable for life. However, nothing is ever constant.

Over the 4,500 million years since the Earth was formed the drag exerted on our planet by gravity of the nearby Moon has slowed its rotation. This, coupled with the gravitational pull of the Sun, means that eventually, thousands of millions of years into the future our Earth's rotation will have slowed sufficiently that one year may be made up of only two or three days. By then, however, the internal heat that drives tectonic activity on Earth will have been lost. As tectonism grinds to a halt, the oceans, whose hydrogen is constantly being replenished by volcanism, will gradually be lost to space. Harmful radiation from the Sun will reach the surface as the atmosphere loses its ability to shield us. As if that wasn't enough, the Sun too will undergo dramatic changes.

5,000 million years into the future, as it runs out of the hydrogen fuel it needs to drive the nuclear fusion reactions at its core, the Sun will cool and swell up into a huge, red giant star. It will be so vast that the inner planets Mercury and Venus will be consumed as it swells. Earth should be spared although it is unlikely that anybody, or anything, will be around to witness these events. Earth will have been already geologically dead for millions of years.

Acknowledgements

Landscapes From Stone *would like to extend their thanks to all their collegues at the Geological Surveys in Belfast and Dublin for their help and advice during the writing, drafting and publication of this book. Various individuals gave advice on the geology of specific regions; Barry Long (Ox Mountains, South Donegal, North Donegal and the Donegal Highlands), Ian Mitchell (Clogher Valley, Erne Lakelands), Conor Mc Dermott (West Breifne), Pat O'Connor (Mourne, Gullion and Cooley), and Terry Johnston (The Sperrins and The Foyle). Their comments, and those of Enda Gallagher, were invaluable and greatly improved the accuracy of the information in this book. John Arthurs and Peadar Mc Ardle, our two Directors, are thanked for their unwavering support for the* **Landscapes From Stone** *project from its inception.*

The Special Support Programme for Peace and Reconciliation is acknowledged as the primary source of funding for this publication. We sincerely hope that we have helped further the aims of the programme by illustrating how our landscapes and our geology give us all something we can acknowledge as our own and of which we can all be justly proud. Local government councils from across the 12 county area are also gratefully acknowledged for their support and encouragement for this project.

Various organisations are also acknowledged as the source of some of the photographs used in this book: 1, 36, 68, 74, 95 - Environment & Heritage Service (Department of the Environment for N. Ireland); 25, 96 - Bord Fáilte (Irish Tourist Board); 65, 93 - Northern Ireland Tourist Board; 87, 90 - Lough Neagh Tourism

The route maps used throughout the book were adapted from the 1:250,000 Scale Ireland (North), Ireland (West) and Ireland (East) Holiday maps published by the Ordnance Survey of N. Ireland by permission of the Controller of Her Majesty's Stationery Office © Crown Copyright, Permit No 500004 and by the Ordnance Survey of Ireland Permit No 7989 © Government of Ireland. Poetry by Seamus Heaney reproduced from "Opened Ground" by permission of the author and Faber & Faber Ltd as publishers throughout the world excluding the USA.

Landscapes From Stone *is a project operated jointly by the Geological Survey of Ireland and the Geological Survey of Northern Ireland. Funded by the Special Support Programme for Peace and Reconciliation, INTERREG and a consortium of local government councils it aims to develop popular literature on the geology and landscapes of Northern Ireland and the border counties of the Republic of Ireland. It also aims to promote and market the geology of the region to the wider, international geological community as a world-class field study destination. The project team can be contacted at the addresses given top right.*

Further Interest

The Geological Surveys publish a series of maps, memoirs, reports and popular publications on the geology and landscapes of Ireland.

For further details of publications on the geology of Northern Ireland please contact the Geological Survey of Northern Ireland, Colby House, Stranmillis Court, Belfast, BT9 5BF or telephone 9038 8462 (prefix 028 from Great Britain, 048 from the Republic of Ireland, ++4428 from overseas). GSNI can also be contacted by fax on 9038 8461 or by e-mail on gsni@detini.gov.uk

For further details of publications on the geology of the Republic of Ireland please contact Geological Survey of Ireland, Beggars Bush, Haddington Road, Dublin 4 or telephone 01 678 200 (prefix ++353 from outside the Republic) or Locall 1890 443311. GSI can also be contacted by fax on 01 678 2549 or by e-mail on gsisales@gsi.ie

The Authors

Dr. Patrick J. Mc Keever is a geologist with the Geological Survey of Northern Ireland. He graduated with a PhD from the Queen's University of Belfast before undertaking hydrocarbon-related research at the University of Manchester. He is passionate about bringing the wonders of geology to the non-specialist and has written several popular-style publications on the geology of Ireland.

Janis Smyth is a graphic designer and illustrator with the Geological Survey of Northern Ireland. She graduated with a MDes(RCA) from the Royal College of Art, London. She has worked in various design fields and is enthusiastic about using her skills to help bring unusual or complicated scientific concepts to the general public.